HEART OF THE WILD

HEART OF THE WILD
Chet Schwarzkopf

ILLUSTRATIONS BY WAYNE TRIMM

DOUBLEDAY & COMPANY, INC.
GARDEN CITY, NEW YORK
1962

Library of Congress Catalog Card Number 62–11431
Copyright © 1962 by Chet Schwarzkopf
All Rights Reserved
Printed in the United States of America
First Edition

AUTHOR'S NOTE

There is, along the coast of northwestern California, a land whose like is nowhere else on earth. Here tower noble redwood trees that have known life since the shepherds' star —patriarchs to whose cathedral aisles men have come to wonder and worship. It is a land of rugged mountains, clean-watered rivers, and lush valleys; and it is here that this book of wild animal stories is set.

One of the book's prime objectives is to evoke sympathy and understanding for our friends of the woods and waters. The stories are founded as much upon fact as was possible for man, the outsider, to do. Of necessity, there were many gaps to fill, since our knowledge, at best, is faulty.

In the lore of the many-tribed Algonquin Indians, there exists a god called Manitou, whose special care is to watch over all wild things. This book mentions Manitou often, and with respect.

C.S.

Contents

HEART OF THE WILD

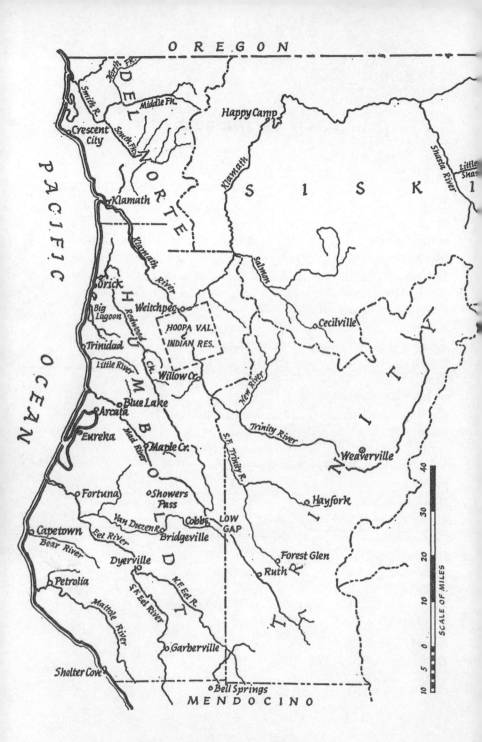

Of Redwood Glens and Waters

Like a far-flung tapestry, the tawny slopes of the uplands of Eaton Roughs caught the harbinger of a California summer dawn. To the east, timbered heights of the Trinity Mountains silhouetted aquamarine against the coming of the sun. Fleeces of mist drifted through Douglas fir dells on the nearby hillsides. And in a secluded glen, a group of deer browsed at breakfast.

Deep in the dimness of the gorge below, the Van Duzen River—that naturalist's Eldorado born in the fastness of the Redwood Empire mountains—sounded its reveille in draughty baritone. Hush-wing, the great horned owl, last of his tribe to seek shelter for the day, broad-winged across the blueness of the canyon depths and merged into the anonymity of the forest at dawn. In an oak copse, a thrush tunkled liquid notes of welcome to another day.

High above the far end of the slope's sweep, a sentinel rock loomed sheer against the awakening sky. So huge was this pinnacle that it might have been a cliff, or the core of an ancient volcanic cone, long since eroded down to naked rock. There it stood, ageless, historic, a reminder to living things that their generations came and went with the seasons—and that once, aeons ago, forces mightier than imagination wrought Eaton Roughs Gorge out of the turbulence of a younger world. And in a tree, atop sentinel rock a thousand feet above the bottom of the gorge, an eagle flexed his wings in the brightening light, unburdened by the briefness of his life's hour against the Infinite.

At the base of sentinel rock, the Van Duzen River tore

through its narrows and plunged into a hole whose depths refracted the blue-green of snow water. Rocks the size of freight cars were scattered about the hole and up and down the gorge, as if fabled Red Bunyan of the redwoods had tossed them casually about when his job was finished.

In wintertime, desolation rules Eaton Roughs. Wild water roars down the gorge, crashes through the narrows and swirls out of the hole, scouring it ever deeper into the rocks that form its bed. Snow is on the ground, and most living creatures have either gone away or sleep in their abodes, safe from the fury of the elements.

But now the benignity of summer was upon the land. Hill slopes already were browning in the semirainless season, and life was astir in every tree, thicket, and clearing. And in the river itself, young rainbow trout raced to and fro to dimple the surface of calm corners, while their elders lurked deep in the coolness of the larger pools.

Gone were the salmon that battered their way up the canyon as far as the narrows every fall and winter, to spawn and die. Their progeny now played among the young trout, darting in search of food that they might attain proper size and go down to the sea to mature. Nor was it given them to know that, four years hence, they too must return to the waters of their birth to procreate and die, in accord with Nature's immutable decree.

The rainbow trout were more fortunate than their salmon half cousins, since it was their privilege to live perhaps a dozen years, and even spawn several times without fatality. They, too, went down to the sea for the most part—to return a year or two later as steelhead trout, a game fish ranked among the nobility. Big were these steelhead-rainbows, upward of two feet in length, and stronger than the salmon, for they could conquer the Van Duzen River's narrows and go into its very headwaters if they desired; nor would they die from the rigors of their spawning saga.

Certain of these steelhead followed a cycle that differed

from the main runs. These would come in from the sea in springtime, but not to spawn. Rather, they seemed to forsake salt water and go back to the life of stream rainbows. Most of them would lose that salmon-silveryness which comes from living in the ocean and color up again in true rainbow raiment. These were the elders of the species that lurked in the larger holes, principal among which was that deep one at the foot of the narrows.

The sheer walls of the gorge towered over the narrows hole, while above the entire scene, sentinel rock caught the first rays of the rising sun. The eagle spread his wings and sailed across the canyon. His keen eyes penetrated through the mistiness that lay wraithlike over the hole, and in the clearness of its depths he could see a number of great trout, each with its nose pointed upstream, watching for food. Like all predatory creatures in the Eaton Roughs region, the eagle was interested in those trout. But he knew his chances of catching anything there were remote, and so he turned his attention to the more immediate possibilities of the open slope.

. . . The hare was large and wary, as befitted one of his kind who had survived several years of life. He advanced from his shelter under a berry bramble one hop at a time, nose and ears twitching, alert for the first sign of danger. Once he thumped a hind foot on the ground and listened. But all seemed serene, while the thrush continued to sing in its oak copse. He nibbled at a tuft of green grass by the north side of a rock, then advanced farther into the open, where certain appetite-whetting herbs were to be found. He would pause every few hops to look, listen, and smell. Thus he had prospered in a world to which his kind is prey.

A challenging odor wafted across the downs, carried by the breeze that comes with sunrise. The hare sniffed it and thumped his hind feet several times in rage. That young usurper from the lower slope was about again. He followed the smell and in a few moments came upon a hare who was somewhat smaller than himself but who did not seem impressed.

The older hare made straight for his rival. The younger animal stood his ground. In the clash that followed, neither of them heard the whistle of descending pinions until it was too late. Before they could break apart, the eagle was upon them.

Although the eagle might have taken both hares had he chosen, he seized the larger and rose into the sparkling air with flapping wing strokes, while his victim writhed and screamed in his talons. Back atop the pinnacle, he dispatched the hare with one crunch of a stone-crusher beak, and settled to his meal. But even as he ate, he noticed an otter gliding sinuously over and around the rocks beside the narrows hole, far below.

Lutra the otter was after his morning meal, and the deep hole was one of his favorite hunting places. Well did he know every cranny beneath its surface, even to a grottolike cave that extended under a thirty-foot rock into the hole's darkest depths. Here it was that the trout hid when enemies threatened or when the sun shone too brightly upon the water as it crossed the gorge at midday. Light was touching the top sides of the gorge now, and from a position of vantage between two logs above the water line, Lutra could see the big rainbows moving about with leisurely strokes of their broad, spotted tails. He began to quiver, and his eyes glowed.

Suddenly the otter plunged into the hole with a splash, like a pitched boulder. Panic-stricken, the trout scattered in every direction—but a majority of them made for the grotto-cave under the rock. This was what Lutra wanted. Almost as quickly as one of the trout, he swerved and shot down into the blue darkness of the hiding place. In the scattering of big bodies that followed, he clamped his teeth onto one, and strove to break its back. But the rainbow trout was large and powerful—although the otter was as big

Wayne Trimm

as a water spaniel. In the struggle that followed, Lutra clamped his legs about the madly thrashing fish and shifted his teeth grip to the back of its head. One deep bite and it was over. He rose to the surface with his quivering catch and took a long breath. Killing fish this size was strenuous work. Then he took it ashore, where he backed onto a sand bar to eat.

Lutra was aware that the eagle had been watching him and he saw the big bird launch its swoop downward long before he could hear the whistle of its pinions. He seized his fish, ran along the beach to the lower end of the hole, and tossed it into the fast water that spilled downward into a rapid. He glanced up at his adversary with a snarl and plunged into the water after the trout.

Thwarted, the eagle banked and beat his way upward toward his pinnacle again. Downstream, Lutra emerged from slower water at the foot of the rapid, the trout in his mouth, and retreated under a log jam. There he proceeded to eat his catch, eyes gleaming angry red in the semi-darkness. He had been through all this before.

A fierce-eyed head with tufted ears looked down from a tangle of brush overlooking the narrows hole. Ahk-weesh the bobcat wanted a trout for himself. He watched Lutra drag his fish ashore below the rapid and retreat under the log jam. No use trying to rob him, for he would again take to the water—an element Ahk-weesh disliked.

Keeping under the half light of the big rock's overhang, the bobcat sneaked to the water's edge, jumped lightly onto a flat ledge just offshore, and crouched immobile as a stuffed replica. Deep water came to the ledge's side. Ahk-weesh knew this, and knew if he waited long enough, one of the big fish would swim within reach—especially now, before the dawn dimness retreated.

A ten-pound rainbow trout broke water out in the hole with a skittering slash. Another shot past Ahk-weesh's ledge with a surge that made the surface bulge. Still another leaped into the waterfall where it plunged into the hole and seized a hapless crawfish on its way down. Ahk-weesh's eyes dilated, but he did not move.

By the opposite side of the hole, on the sand spit recently vacated by Lutra, a large, tawny animal appeared, followed by two smaller ones of the same breed. A female cougar, or mountain lion, had arrived with her kits to look at the fish and, perhaps, snag an unwary one out of the rapids if the chance offered. The cougar looked about intently and sniffed the air. It was redolent with information. Not only did she smell Lutra and Ahk-weesh, but deer, raccoons, and mink, while a faint odor of bear wafted from below. But she did not see Ahk-weesh, flattened on his ledge, for the bobcat did not so much as twitch a hair. Well did he know the rule of the wilderness—lie quietly, and you will not be observed.

Downstream, perhaps eighty yards, a black bulk was shuffling along, watching the riffles and peering into pools. It was not salmon time, but the bear knew that salmon-size trout were to be found in the Van Duzen River during summer's low water. And these, while difficult to catch, made choice eating. The bear waded into the stream and stood still, poised tensely. For some ten minutes she waited, immobile as a rock. Then, like a minor explosion, her paw tore the water.

A bulky, reddish-sided trout flew through the air and landed flopping on the bank. Before the bear could retrieve it, her cub burst out of the brush and pounced upon it, growling. She watched his antics with the fond tolerance of mother love but did not try to share the meal. Then she lumbered upstream until she came to the foot of the rapids that spilled out of the narrows hole, where she waded in again.

Up at the hole, Ahk-weesh watched from his ledge while the cougar tensed on the sand bar. High on the pinnacle overhead, the eagle leaned out and cocked his head like an attentive dog, the better to observe. But the bear paid them no heed, if indeed she saw them at all. She had business at hand.

The sun was now well into the sky. The somber depths of the gorge were becoming brighter as the light advanced down its flank. Small birds were chirping and twittering. A water ouzel took up its station beside an eddy below the bear and began diving after hellgrammites and water larvae. Although this bird could fly with the swift, erratic flight of a bat, it also could swim underwater by beating its wings as if in flight. Several times it slipped into the water, popped up with its prey in its beak and took off—to land on some stones beneath a dripping overhang and eat at its leisure.

. . . Atop the pinnacle, the eagle suddenly spread his wings and flew away. He did not wheel back and forth, as he would when on the hunt, but proceeded straight across the canyon and into the hills. Before long, a pair of mountain jays—sentries of the wilderness—set up a clamor in the woods above the gorge. Their cries might have said "Owl! Owl!" for they always liked to discover Hush-wing at roost and shout his presence to the rest of the world. But they might have seen something else.

Their noise came faintly to the cougar's ears over the rush of the water. She transferred her attention from the trout, and listened intently. Then she sprang atop a rock and peered in the direction of the jays' warning. For a moment she took stock. Then, as if she had spoken a command, her kits melted into the brush as one animal, and she followed.

Ahk-weesh let his yellow eyes shift in the direction of the jays' yammering, while one ear twitched involuntarily. He hated to give up his ledge—twice a big trout had come almost within seizing range. But there was no mistaking that alarm. Light as down, he sprang ashore, while the brush no more than flicked as he disappeared into hiding.

Lutra left what remained of his trout under the log jam and slipped into the water without a ripple—in contrast to his splash at the hole when he was on the hunt. A quarter mile downstream, he emerged and retreated into his den for the day.

Only the mother bear seemed oblivious to the withdrawal that was taking place around her. Rocklike, she poised in the water, waiting for another big trout to go by. Perhaps, because of her place at the foot of the rapids, she was too close to the water's roar to hear the jays. Some sixty yards away, her cub was enjoying his fish. To him, the clacking of the birds meant nothing. He was engrossed in his repast.

The odor was coming down from a small draw that opened into the gorge, not far below the cub. It reached him, and he stopped eating and raised his head, the better to sniff it. A rock came clattering down the draw and bounded into the underbrush. Some large creature was approaching, and its emanation was hostile. About then, the cub decided he wanted his mother. He grabbed a last hasty mouthful of trout and left, whimpering and floundering around about the rocks until he rejoined her.

The mother bear jerked her head to attention, for with arrival of the cub had come the first trace of odor. She snorted, pushed her offspring into the water, and all but shoved him across the stream. There was nothing clumsy or ambling about her movements now. In seconds, the two of them were out of sight and climbing toward the timber.

In the suddenly vacated area about the narrows hole, only the water ouzel continued its quest in peace. Unseen eyes were watching—and would continue to watch—but to all appearance, the place was enjoying a tranquil morning.

Had the two men noticed it when they dropped down from the mouth of the little draw and approached the Van Duzen River, they could have read quite a story from the tracks in the sand. But they did not even see the remains of the cub's trout, nor had they paid any attention to the

jays. They were intent only upon the big trout hole upstream and started for it at once.

All day, the men remained at the narrows hole. For a
time, they cast with spinners, and one of them hooked a
husky rainbow—only to lose it after much splashing and
shouting. Then as the midday sun shone down the gorge
and upon the hole, they built a fire, ate lunch, and basked
in the sunlight.

The water ouzel caught their attention about then, and
one of them amused himself shooting at it with a target
pistol until, after a time, the little bird disappeared. After
that, no wild creatures—even the jays—came near the hole.

When afternoon shadows began to darken the water, the
men resumed fishing—this time with bait. One of them
jumped onto Ahk-weesh's vacated ledge and cast his hook
into the deep water in front of the underwater cave. Before
long, he was whooping hoarsely as the line cut across the
hole with an audible hiss and headed for the overflow end.
Too late, he discovered the fish's intentions. A spade-
shaped tail flashed in the rapids—and it was over. He
reeled in what was left of his line, swearing and lamenting.

Later, he hooked another and managed to horse it ashore
by main strength, abetted by a stout line. Still later, as
shadows were turning blue, the other man beached a noble
red-side that had taken issue with a spinner. Whereupon
they gathered up their gear and left. It was a long, uphill
pull back to their automobile.

For some time after the invaders went away, the rushing
of the river was the only movement at the narrows hole. Not
even a trout broke the surface of the darkening water. The
pinnacle of sentinel rock no longer reflected the sun's rays.
Across the gorge and toward the skyline, the timbered
slopes of the Trinity Mountains shone in the retreating sunlight, while shadows crept up their flanks.

Almost unnoticed, the eagle returned to his tree atop
sentinel rock. Day birds chattered in subdued motif in the

trees below, but the jays had turned silent for the night. Down by the hole's edge, Ahk-weesh appeared suddenly. He sniffed at the man tracks and the fire they had left smoldering, and paused to look at his ledge. About that time, the first big fish broke water so near to the ledge that it splashed spray upon it. That was enough. Ahk-weesh leaped onto the ledge and froze to immobility.

Across the hole, a raccoon trotted along the beach looking for frogs and crawdads. Downstream, Lutra slid into the water like an apparition and began working toward the narrows hole. He was in no hurry. There would be good hunting all the way. He stopped to look at the cub's abandoned fish, now dry and shriveling, and turned away in disdain. Let the coyotes have it. . . .

Up in their secluded glen by the edge of the open slopes, the little herd of deer were making ready for their evening's forage. They had watched the men go by and return, noisy of voice and foot. They had listened to the men's excited yelling and bang-banging when they encountered a rattlesnake. Now all was quiet in Eaton Roughs.

On a wooded ridge in back of the deer, the cougar was planning the night's hunt for herself and kits—which was to include a foray after the deer. But the deer were well aware of that. It was all part of the business of life, wherein the fittest shall survive. So always had it been. . . .

Up in the timber across the Van Duzen River, on the far side of Eaton Roughs, the mother bear watched the first shadows of dusk creep up from the darkening gorge. This meant little to her, since her eyesight was not keen. But her ears had told her of the events of the day—among which was the departure of the men—while her nose quivered to the scent of succulent flesh to be hunted and plant fruit to be picked. She grunted at her cub and started down the mountain.

High in the air over the dim depths of the canyon, Hush-wing floated away from the sheltering forest he had sought at dawn—first of his tribe to be out in the owl dusk that ushers in the night. Wings rigid, he coasted down into the gorge like a plane coming in to its airport—to land beside the stream for a drink of water and a quick spruce-up. Ahk-weesh, Lutra, and the raccoon all saw him and, in their way, acknowledged his kingship of the night by letting him alone.

The wind that skirts the edge of nightfall came up canyon from the centuries-old redwoods below, and soughed through the fir forests on the mountainside. The tawniness of Eaton Roughs upland was fading into starlit gray. Down in its gorge, the Van Duzen River rendered its vesper song, cool and clean-toned as the whispered benediction of the forest wind above.

Babe in the Woods

It was after dusk of a late spring evening when Moklah, the raccoon cub, got his first look at the world. He was a month old now and had been able to see since his eyes opened on his nineteenth day of life. But until this time, Moklah did not know anything existed outside of his birthplace in a storm-blasted hollow trunk in a grove of California redwoods.

Moonbeams slanted between the great trees and spread silver upon forest aisles, while somewhere among the fern vales a brook tunkled the gladness of new life. Although the beauty of his Van Duzen River valley was beyond Moklah's scope, he stared round-eyed at this revelation, sniffed its multitude of odors, and listened to the muted sounds of night. This was good, he felt, and must be investigated without delay, while memories as old as his tribe stirred anew. Now to see more of it. . . .

He left the hollow and climbed out onto the stub of a limb. Before long, he saw his mother trot across the clearing below and scurry up the tall trunk that had sheltered her young each spring.

And then Moklah got a surprise. Mother raccoon was not pleased to find the most precocious of her four sprites out of bounds. She refused to acknowledge his chirr of greeting, cuffed him smartly, and drove him inside . . . for Moklah's freshly discovered world of wonder contained enemies, among whom was Hush-wing, the great horned owl, who had a taste for young raccoon.

For a time, Moklah sulked in a corner of the family's

spacious nest, while the other three cubs squabbled sociably over a crawfish their mother had brought from the stream, and then settled down to nursing. Truth was, Moklah had eaten most of a previous crawfish which, topped with a lusty portion of milk, afforded him time out for a huff.

But to mother raccoon, it was an indication that the hour was at hand when she must lead her brood from the shelter of the trunk and make them acquainted with the world outside. Also, one of the basic laws of raccoondom decrees that food must be washed in water, if available, and her youngsters were beginning to want solid diet.

In the hour following midnight—that interlude of quiet between eventime's hunting and the foray before dawn— she coaxed her cubs out onto the stub beside the hollow's entrance. Moklah went first, his chastisement of a few hours before forgotten; but one of his sisters, smallest of the family, held back and whimpered at this departure from accepted rote. And so the matter went no farther than a preview of things to come.

The next night, mother raccoon decided on positive measures. When midnight's hush was upon the forest, she led all four of the cubs outside, and started down. First, they had to descend to a bole, then climb back to the entrance of the hollow, to learn how it was done. Moklah did this without trouble, his sensitive paws gripping the weathered wood like a squirrel's toes. Flexible as human hands were these small, five-fingered paws, and already they were endowed with surprising strength. He was impatient to get to the ground below, with its alluring odors, and only his mother's command kept him from leaving the rest and going down on his own.

Again little sister was the holdback. She descended inch by inch, while the rest of the family waited, and mother raccoon aided and scolded by turns. First on the ground was Moklah, who scampered into a bed of ferns where several matters awaited investigation. A salamander retreated under a pile of last year's leaves, from which he extracted it with a whicker of joy.

Now what to do? Moklah picked up the squirming creature in his jaws, but something was not right. Something had to be done before this morsel was ready to eat. He espied an inch-deep puddle beside the trunk. Here, instinct told him, was the missing essential. He took the salamander to the puddle and washed it thoroughly, although his prey had emerged from water only moments before.

Mother raccoon saw him, and dropped to the ground with two of the youngsters to inspect Moklah's catch. On a burl of the trunk, five feet above ground, little sister quavered her protest at this desertion. As she did, a shadow swooped down, silent as a falling leaf, and seized her. Too late, mother raccoon sprang for the burl. Hush-wing was off for his haunt, and the last the raccoon family heard from its luckless member was a wail receding among the trees.

The survivors climbed back into their shelter in a frightened hurry. But Moklah, despite the demoralization of this air attack, managed to hold onto his salamander. Later, in the safety of the hollow, he ate it and completed his first step toward self-support.

Nightly thereafter, the young raccoons visited the ground, but their mother saw to it that they stayed together. They caught fat frogs and succulent crawfish in the stream, washing every mouthful in the water it came from. They splashed merrily in the riffles, or romped on the forest greens—three furry little elfins with black burglar masks across their eyes—while their parent kept watch.

Bit by bit they learned, as the days lengthened toward summer—how to poke about rotting logs and stumps for insect grubs; how to catch meadow mice under the grass; how to dig for bulbs and roots in the glades; how to feel beneath underwater stones with their handlike paws for a

hiding crawfish or frog. Also, they learned that a farm a half mile away had dogs that bore watching.

Above all else in the world, one thing was impressed upon the developing faculties of the three youngsters—mankind was an enemy worse and more cunning than Hush-wing or any dogs. The odor of human beings warned of a foe that must always be avoided—for men's guns and dogs had killed their father before they were born, leaving mother raccoon to raise her family alone.

On the other hand, however, human beings were strangely stupid at times and therefore could be outgeneraled, while their orchards and gardens produced excellent food. But this was the final course in their education—not to be taken up until all else was mastered and understood.

A change was occurring in the Van Duzen River valley as summer grew lush and warm and the three young raccoons were almost weaned. Mankind seemed to be invading their habitat as never before, making a great deal of noise and taking away the redwood trees. It was alarming, but the men always left at night and stayed away.

The cubs had grown past quarter size, and the timbermen were approaching closer to the raccoons' hollow trunk each day, when mother raccoon decided reluctantly to find a safer location. The noise was so near now that it disturbed her rest—but worst of all was her fear of the unknown.

On what might have been the family's final day before leaving their hollow, the loggers arrived at a tall redwood not over seventy feet away. They studied the situation and decided to cut the tree so that it would crush the dead trunk on its way down—which would help "bed" the giant against the shattering effect of its fall. All of which was good logging, and they set to work.

Mother raccoon was increasingly worried at the sound of voices and the chug of the saw's gas engine so near, but there was nothing she could do about it until nightfall.

Once, when one of the crew bludgeoned the base of the hollow, she stood over her brood, wide-eyed with fear.

The engine's noise continued all morning, and the raccoons had become so accustomed to it that they stirred uneasily when it stopped—to be followed by ringing blows at irregular intervals. Suddenly the blows ceased, and the men's voices shouted "TIMMBERRR!" It was such a terrifying outcry that mother raccoon rose to her feet again—just as a scatter of shotlike cracks rose to a volley. And that was the last she knew.

After a timeless interval, Moklah revived enough to realize that something was terribly wrong. He whimpered in pain, and tried to raise his head to see what had happened, but he was pinned under crushed wood and green fronds. Somewhere amid the wreckage he could smell his mother and family, but the odor repelled him.

Feebly at first, then with returning consciousness, he tried to dig his way out. He became aware of the greenery about him but could not comprehend it, since he associated that with the ground and not the dead trunk. A fine dust from the disintegrated hollow almost choked him at times and irritated his eyes. He was becoming more and more thirsty, while ants crawling through the debris in the summer night discovered him, and a few crawled over his face.

But the ants, for the most part, seemed interested in other things. Moklah was frightened and confused. The smell of his family was becoming more pronounced and abhorrent. His conscious self did not understand why this should be, but deep within him, instinct recognized the emanations of death.

Claw and try though Moklah might, there seemed no way to free himself. His pain was increasing, for he had a mashed hind paw, while his breath came in gasps from a couple of broken ribs. As night wore on, his efforts slackened, and toward morning he went into a comalike sleep.

For the next day and night, Moklah lay in his prison,

trying at times to get out, but lapsing more and more into a half torpor. The ants were crawling over him in greater numbers now, while the odor of his family was strong and sickening. Toward the last, a merciful numbness descended upon him like fog and blotted out his misery.

On the second morning, the loggers started work on the fallen monarch with much clangor of machinery and tools. A cleanup crew hacked through the branches, while a bulldozer pushed deeper into the tangle at the remains of the raccoons' hollow trunk, to clear the way for a saw. As it did, the demolished wood near Moklah was ripped loose, and sunlight shone through upon the nearly dead young raccoon.

Moklah raised his head, unaware even of the noise. He squirmed feebly to get away from the light, but he was cornered in a pocket, one side of which had been laid open within inches of his body. Fresh air penetrated through to him for the first time since he had been buried alive. With it came the cool, clean scent of water. A man almost stepped on his face once, but Moklah was too far gone to take fright. Then, abruptly, the men left.

In the quiet that ensued, instinct came to the rescue. Moklah crawled blindly out of his trap and started for the creek. He no longer knew he was thirsty, but a power beyond his will was leading him toward the water scent. The loggers were all at lunch, and no one saw him as he reached the edge of a pool and drank.

For the rest of the afternoon, Moklah lay under a thicket of azaleas. When the woods quieted at dusk, he had cleared up enough to realize he was hungry and that his family was missing. Again he went to the stream, where he drank and washed. Then, feeling somewhat better, he set out to get food and find his mother. Food he found, although in poor amount, since he had not had time to master the fundamentals of self-support. But he never saw any of his family again, nor did he go near the wreckage of his birthplace.

Morning found Moklah in a quandary. His ribs and leg were paining, and he had not traveled far. It was daylight before he chose an alder thicket and crawled under a pile of flotsam left by winter floods. And there he hid, a lonely and frightened young thing, unable to fathom the tragedy that had changed his world, while the loggers shouted and worked a quarter mile away.

It was only after several nights of wandering, and concealment as best he could during daytime, that Moklah finally strayed into a rocky ravine and found a hollow log that smelled of his own kind. He limped into it without hesitation, and curled up in a corner. His ribs pained so much that he did not want to climb, while his injured leg had developed a running sore. He was hungry and sick, and the memory of his mother was slipping away. All he knew was that he wanted something and it was not there.

Moklah had no way of knowing that the raccoon odor in this log came from his father whom he never had seen. Nor had any other raccoons taken over this sweep of the Van Duzen Valley which had belonged to his parents. The time for migrants looking for a place to settle would come later. For the present, Moklah was let alone, and he did not realize his inherited locale had value.

Fortunately, Moklah's ravine was outside the loggers' workings, although it was not far from a farm. But to the homeless youngster, neither the new-found log nor any other place seemed satisfactory. He was licking his festered leg a great deal now, which tended to upset him. He thinned down still further, and often he whimpered to himself in the loneliness of his lair—a forlorn babe in the woods, awaiting he knew not what. That the summer was in full bloom and the woods at their best was lost upon him. And a prowling bobcat that chased him at every opportunity did not help the situation. Moklah was thoroughly miserable.

One night, when he was dragging about in quest of

food, Moklah came upon a strange sight. There, snarling and hissing at something that had hold of one foreleg, was his tormentor, Ahk-weesh the bobcat. Moklah forgot his own troubles for the moment and sat down to watch. As he did, an inner prompting warned him that here was a lesson to observe and remember—that the smell of steel traps was an odor associated with mankind.

It was then he saw the chicken. Ahk-weesh had been carrying it when he stepped into the trap. Now, freed and still alive, the chicken was groping to and fro in the dark. It came toward Moklah with halting jerks. He backed away at first, but this time instinct was telling him there was nothing to fear—also, this bird smelled better than anything he had been able to catch. He seized it with his youngster's teeth and, although the chicken weighed more than himself, dragged it into the brush out of the bobcat's sight. And there Moklah found how hungry he had been.

That ill-fated chicken marked the turning point in Moklah's life. He slept soundly all day, gorged to repletion, and when he awakened, his ribs and leg felt better. And such is the resiliency of the young that he forgot all about his injuries and healed up in a week.

After that windfall, Moklah began to find himself. No longer did that bobcat chase him, for its hide was drying on the south side of the farmer's barn. He began to acquire additional knowledge—how to ambush rabbits; that juicy ears of corn could be taken from the farm garden in spite of the dogs—and best of all, he caught his first trout! This last came purely by accident, when he was feeling under a rock for crawfish. The trout was not a large one, but its discovery opened a new horizon. Thereafter, he fared increasingly well and began to put on weight.

One night, toward late summer, he ran afoul of near-disaster. A hollow trunk, not unlike the one of his birth, seemed to contain an inviting mixture of odors. Since this called for investigation, he started to climb it.

Had Hush-wing waited until the half-grown raccoon was well up into his citadel, Moklah's career might have ended then and there. As it was, a broad-winged apparition swooped down almost at once, and struck him an agonizing blow. Moklah had a momentary glimpse of a big, yellow-eyed head that reminded him of Ahk-weesh, while a murderous beak clop-clopped within an inch of his eyes.

Instinct leapt to Moklah's rescue. He covered his face and fell to the ground, while Hush-wing's mate and their two almost grown progeny joined the chase. Fortunately, a thicket of wild blackberries was alongside, and he scurried under its protecting brambles as fast as he could go. Nor was he allowed to come out until broad daylight. After that, Moklah never trespassed upon the horned owls' household again.

When he got back to his hollow log, hungry and nursing a raw slash across his shoulders, another surprise awaited him. A large male or "boar" raccoon had taken possession. His malevolent eyes glinted reddish from the log's depths. Moklah hesitated at the other's growl. Here was the first of his species he had seen since the world changed. He chirred softly, for he would have liked nothing better than the company of his own kind.

But no answering whinny came from the log. A rasping snarl, and Moklah was bowled over by the enemy's rush. He scrambled to his feet, protesting, while the big boar pounced upon him and punished him savagely. Again and again he was knocked down in his effort to flee from this enemy that should have been a friend.

A skunk's den under the rocks, where his foe could not enter, was all that saved Moklah—nor could he stay there long, for Che-num, its owner, was at home. Not that the skunk proposed to use his spray inside the den, but he was as large as Moklah and willing to do battle—and once at grips, anything could happen.

Moklah peeked from the den's entrance—to find that the

enemy, wise in the ways of Che-num, had left. Whereupon
he bolted out and climbed the nearest tree, where he hid
all day. But his eyes shone red as he tended his wounds,
and his seldom used growl took on a deeper note. Moklah
was beginning to grow up.

In fact, Moklah had to grow up. The arrival of the big
boar brought about many changes. No longer did Moklah
own the woods, nor could he feel free to hunt and fish as
he chose. Anywhere he went, that hateful foe might come
onto the scene, and always he lusted to kill.

After some looking about, Moklah located a strategic
den high among the rocks near the head of the ravine—
only to be found by the big boar, sure this time of his kill.
But Moklah fought with the savageness of his race when
cornered. He retreated into a nook where the foe could not
reach him, but where his own sharp teeth could slash an
exploring paw. And so the issue was postponed until another time.

Moklah was old enough by now to realize that the immediate area could not harbor two male raccoons, but he was
not old enough to know that there were other places to
which he could move. Besides, he felt that this particular
slope of the valley was his by right of domain. He growled
a still deeper note as he dressed his hurts, and his eyes
gleamed with a killing-red hate.

Moklah knew enough, however, to bide his time. He
shifted to a pasture on the opposite side of the farm and
took up residence in a lone oak tree that had a deep hollow.
Here he was let alone.

Snow comes rarely to the lower Van Duzen Valley, and
Moklah, like the rest of his tribe in the coastal redwoods,
did not go into lengthy hibernation. He would sleep for two
or three days during the peak of the winter storms, but
when returning sunlight warmed his oak tree, he was out
and around again. The streams were high, and food was
none too plentiful, although frogs might emerge after a

rain, while rodents could be dug out of their winter quarters.

About then, he discovered the farmer's barn had an excellent supply of mice, which were available if he was careful. Also, the big boar was afraid to enter the barn, but filched an occasional chicken when the chance offered—which kept the farmer in a state of exasperation, and resulted in a couple of noisy 'coon hunts. Several innocent raccoons in other parts of the valley paid with their lives, but the big boar was too crafty; while Moklah in his solitary oak out in the pasture went unnoticed—perhaps because he had not molested poultry, despite that windfall from Ahk-weesh.

In common with all his brethren, Moklah had an insatiable bump of curiosity. In a world bursting with possibilities, all things had to be investigated. Before long, he had accumulated a store of loot in his oak sanctum, including an old radiator cap, several door handles, and a china egg—but the pearl of his cache was a rear-view mirror from a discarded truck. He would fondle this treasure and turn it from side to side, growling occasionally when he saw his own image because that reminded him of the enemy. What Moklah had yet to discover was that the way of the collector is not always smooth.

One night, emboldened by success, he decided to pilfer the tool room of the barn. A covered box in one corner gave out an unusual scent. He peered into a hole in its front to check up. Four tiny kittens, their eyes no more than opened, spat at him with a chorus of "heh-hehs." Moklah was fascinated. He had grown considerably by now and was too large to squeeze into the cat's entryway, which had been cut small to keep dogs out. He reached an exploring paw toward the kittens, and their spitting redoubled. He had no thought of them as prey—they looked like desirable playmates, and he was lonely.

There was a screech behind him. Before Moklah could

get his head and forearm out, the furies of all hell landed upon his back! He jumped backward in confusion, and a claw seared across his eyes. That was enough. No animal, even a bear, will brave the righteous wrath of a mother cat. Moklah fled, like the guilty trespasser he knew he was, while his rider spurred him on and raked clawfuls of fur from his back. When he reached the far side of the barnyard, the cat dropped off with a final dig and turned back, the picture of moral vindication. It was several days before Moklah dared go near the barn again. Men and dogs were to be taken in their place, but this cat-tigress was as beyond reach of reason as the big boar 'coon, whom he occasionally saw from a distance.

Springtime brought disturbing sensations and odors to Moklah. He was nearly matured by now, and weighed better than fifteen pounds. His gray fur was luxuriant and thick, while his sharp face with its black mask across the eyes, gave him an Artful Dodger mien. He was more than a match for most dogs, and no longer feared them as in his cub days. Rather, he avoided them as a matter of policy.

As the weather warmed, Moklah's loneliness increased. Never had he had an opportunity to mingle with his own kind, as a normal raccoon should. The only raccoon he knew was his implacable enemy. Now, however, the first mating urge was upon him, and he began to range farther.

It was then Moklah discovered the big boar's mate had joined him and that the pair had moved into that strategic rock den, high in the ravine, keeping the hollow log below for an annex. The female raccoon proved as belligerent as the big boar himself, and the two of them drove Moklah almost to the farmer's barn before turning back. Again Moklah felt he had been the trespasser, as with Hush-wing and the cat. But the mating scent had stirred his blood as never before, and his hatred for the big boar grew to a fever as his loneliness and desire increased.

The first Moklah knew his hideout had been discovered

was when he heard the big boar scaling the oak, while he was inside. His fur rose in rage, and he met the invader head-on at the entrance to his hollow.

And now Moklah knew the hour had come. He remembered his loot inside the tree, and felt he must defend it to the end. The big boar was quite the larger and stronger, but to Moklah belonged the right of ownership, even though he had no mate.

Moklah's one advantage lay in the hollow that protected him on three sides, and he did not try to force the struggle into the open. Although he fought with courage and cunning beyond his youth, it was not long before the foe's superior resources began to tell. A limb directly below the hollow's entry had given the big boar a point of vantage. From it, he was able to hurl his bulk onto Moklah with deadly effect. Twice, Moklah was seized in a deathlock, while the big boar chopped him mercilessly and all but tore him out of his rampart.

The third time, Moklah had to summon every ounce of his final reserve to batter free and, as he waited panting and bleeding, he began to tremble from reaction. Death leered from the foe's eyes, burning blood-red behind their mask. The finish seemed assured—whereupon the killer broadcasted a blare of triumph.

A dog's bark answered from the farmyard, and another joined in. Moklah always had been silent around his habitation—but now, with the big boar's challenge as a giveaway, the dogs raced yelling to the oak and leaped about its base.

The big boar snarled down at the clamorous pack and knew he had made a mistake. Moklah kept his eyes just above the rim of his hollow to watch, gaining strength from this respite. Then a light left the house, and men hurried toward the uproar at the oak.

As they neared the tree, the big boar cringed, for here came the one enemy he feared with all his being. He charged again at Moklah, wanting only to get inside the hollow now.

Moklah had had time to get his wind. More than that— he sensed the change in the foe and, despite their common peril, took heart. He met the big boar with a clash of teeth against teeth, and threw him back. Again the foe charged, trying with the strength of desperation to force his way inside. Again he was thrown back by a snapping, rending demon that would not be denied.

A beam of light outlined the big boar. He looked down at it with reflector eyes—and the crash of a gun made Moklah jump. But the big boar crumpled and fell to the ground.

The light's beam seared upward again, and a man pounded on the trunk below with a club. Moklah dropped to the bottom of his lair and crouched motionless. Several shots blasted into the hollow's entry in quick succession, causing a deluge of dust and decayed wood to fall on top of him, but Moklah did not move.

Then a man climbed the tree and perched on the limb vacated by the big boar. Moklah listened in an agony of tension, but still he did not move.

The light beam pierced the dust-laden air of the hollow. It searched every cranny and flashed up and down the length of the cavity a number of times. But Moklah was covered with debris shot loose by the bullets, and he lay so still he scarcely breathed.

After a time, the man went down, and Moklah heard voices raised in argument. Then another man came up and he, too, flashed the beam up and down the tree's interior. By now, Moklah's throat was dusty and he was fighting an urge to cough—but he kept quiet as a quail chick in hiding. Finally, the man pitched several chunks of loose wood down the hollow and left. Before long, their voices receded across the pasture.

It was over an hour before Moklah dared come out. And

when he abandoned the oak, he stopped to sniff the blood on the ground—and knew his woods belonged to him once more—this time for good.

It was three nights later, in a moonlit glen under the redwoods, that Moklah found her—a shy little elfin-pixie with a roguish mask across her eyes as if to shield her identity. Nor did she seem able to run quite as fast as himself.

Outside of a permanently ripped ear, and several soon-to heal wounds, Moklah was in excellent fettle again. And here—every iota of his being cried aloud—here was the one he had been looking for! He overtook her with joyous whickerings.

Toward morning, Moklah went up to the den at the head of the rocky ravine. This was one of the best locations in the Van Duzen woods, and he was determined to re-possess it now that he had come into his own. But the late foe's sour-natured spouse had bowed to the change and left—which was all that Moklah wanted, since he had no wish to dispute with females. Nor would he court any others, for the night's events had broken his loneliness, and Moklah had a life-partner to share his domain.

Before long, he would get his loot out of the abandoned oak of his bachelorhood and take it to his mate in their new abode.

Killer Trout

Several springs upwelled in the thousand-year-old twilight of redwood glades and united in a northern California bog to form Mill Creek. Cold and deep, it glided under thickets and wild berry banks across a mile of meadow, cut through a willow covert, and ended its brief flow in Mad River. Toward the last, the creek dallied for fifty yards through a dark, tree-shadowed pool—summer lair of Zar, king-terror of the cutthroat trout in Mill Creek.

A soft cheeping and twittering emanated from a reed bed near the pool's edge. Mother teal was taking her buff-specked babies for their first swim. She cocked a wary eye in all directions at first. Then with a reassuring "eck," she walked into an inch of water. Her six broodlings, true to age-old ritual, followed in single file.

One adventurous mite, fascinated with this new mode of travel, left the family and paddled out toward the far edge of the reeds. At a call from his mother, he turned back. And as he did, the water about him seemed to bulge. One terrified peep, and he vanished in a swirl. The mother and survivors rushed ashore yammering and fled.

In the cool murk of the pool, big Zar, the cutthroat trout, swung back toward his den under a willow bank. He gaped salmonlike jaws as a man might smack his lips. A bulge fluttered below his throat from the duckling's last reflexes before its life thread let go. He gave another gulp to accelerate his victim on its way and with a lash of his spotted square tail shot ahead, scattering a group of medium-sized trout in panic.

Deep into the dark water cruised the killer, a full two feet of him, thick in his midriff like a salmon. His cheeks were reddish, while a purple-pink stripe ran the length of his heavily speckled flanks. On each side of his throat, below the gills, was a bright-red streak almost like a slash— that characteristic mark which gives the cutthroat trout his name.

At the entrance to his lair, Zar settled upon his gold-and-spotted undersides to watch the dimness of the water with cold eyes. His jaws opened and closed in slow rhythm as he breathed. Good hunting was his right, his heritage. He owned the pool.

To Zar belonged that favor which Nature grants only to a chosen few of her life kingdom. He was larger and more powerful than most of his species, and his share of consciousness flamed more fiercely than theirs. Moreover, he knew it and took full advantage.

Zar was a trout of methodical habits. Late each spring, when Mad River began to warm, he would forsake the larger stream and return to the cold brook of his birth. Here, in the shaded depths of Mill Creek pool, he would spend summer and early fall.

When first October rains freshened the stream, a restlessness would come upon Zar. He would return to Mad River and go down to the sea for a change of diet. He would not remain long in salt water; nor would he ascend to mountain gorges on his spawning run, as did his steelhead-rainbow cousins. Rather, he preferred to live and propagate within a few miles of tidewater, where the sea fog darkened the sun and where he could catch young salmon trout on their migration to sea, or feed in the river's lagoon when the surf fish and shrimp were running.

While Zar did not know it, his seasonal returns to Mill Creek pool were causing numbers of false flies and dangerous salmon eggs to concentrate there—as well as various wriggling, shiny things that roused him to murderous rage.

Hard experience had taught him restraint, after several occasions when only his bulk and power saved him from the enemy on shore. And he had had an unpleasant time getting rid of the hooks afterward, a process which involved much gaping and rubbing of jaws against roots.

So when a chunk of salmon roe descended through the water, leaving a milky wake and landing not six feet from his den, Zar looked at it in contempt—although his orange and white underfins twitched with desire when the oily essence wafted toward him.

A few fingerling trout had followed the roe part way down, but they gave up and returned to the safety of shallow water. They craved to tear this tempting morsel apart, but they feared to go too near the killer's lair. True, he may have sired them on the spawning riffles above the bog, where he himself had been born some eight years before. But now they were part of his natural prey—until the survivors grew too large to swallow.

A pair of medium-sized cutthroat trout came along— handsome specimens a foot in length. They glanced toward Zar's den, and stopped to inspect the salmon roe. Out of his lair shot the giant, and they fled. With never a glance at the bait, he turned back.

Presently a larger trout arrived. He, too, kept an eye on Zar's headquarters. Although not over sixteen inches in length, he was a faithful duplicate of the big trout, even to salmon-like jaws and square tail. He circled the bait and nipped off an egg that was loosely attached. He quivered and worked his jaws much as the killer had done when he swallowed the duckling.

In his shelter, Zar watched with cold-eyed interest, but made no move. The other trout opened his mouth wide, engulfed the entire chunk, and scurried off with it. He had gone perhaps five feet when a pull brought him about. Instantly he turned berserk. Up to the surface he shot and flung himself into the air. Ripples ran the length of the pool as the battle began. Down to the bottom he sounded, past Zar's lair with never a look, and away.

Before long he returned, striving with waning strength to get back to the bottom. But the force that had hold of him was pulling him upward with relentless power. After a time, his exhausted slapping sounded on the surface, and he was seen no more. Other trout darted to and fro, and throughout the pool there was unrest.

In a few minutes, another chunk of salmon roe settled on the bottom, emitting oily milk. But the denizens of the water, except for a couple of stupid bullheads, wanted nothing to do with it.

Zar watched the bullheads, now in sole possession of the area in front of his lair. Only their sharp, painful spines kept them out of his stomach—and not always then, for he relished bullhead meat, especially if it was young. They nipped and haggled at the roe until one of them left for the surface, struggling in surprise.

Not long afterward, a piece of white flesh came down, emitting a tasteful odor. Zar quickened to attention. That was fresh bullhead! He slipped out of his shelter to investigate. There it lay—no spines, no head—still vibrating faintly with life. He noted the almost transparent shred that seemed attached to it and paused. Land animals occasionally spilled fresh pieces of fish and frogs into the water, he knew. His jaws quivered as the delectable essence permeated about him.

Cautiously he picked up the piece of flesh and backed toward his lair. He had gone perhaps two feet when he felt it begin to resist. He dropped it instantly—and in the same split second the bait jerked and raced upward. Zar returned sullenly to his shelter, and when the morsel returned he ignored it and drove others away.

Dusk was upon the pool. Down by Zar's lair, the water was turning black. The bullhead bait had lain untouched, except by one of its witless kin that turned cannibal. But now there was a feeling of excitement in the water. Insect nymphs were rising to the surface. A feeding period was commencing.

Zar was restless. So when a large, whitish-gray moth rippled the surface sheen, he rose at once and seized it with a swirl. He had hardly closed his jaws upon it before he realized it was false, and tried to spit it out. At the same instant, the moth jerked and took hold of his jaw with that pulling sting he knew so well.

Wild with rage, he leaped into the air and landed with a whack that ran wavelets the length of the pool. With a great surge, he bore down and raced away, fighting the drag of the moth. At the upper end of the pool he swung about, kicking up foam, and dashed back. At once, the moth's pull weakened, and Zar headed for his den.

The big cutthroat trout was not terrified at being hooked. Rather, he was infuriated and drove deep into his refuge under the willow bank to rid himself of this humbug that was no moth. Into a jungle of roots he pushed, lashing his head back and forth. In a matter of seconds the light leader snapped.

Zar lay quietly and watched the line pulling at the tangle into which he had worked it. Finally it went limp and seemed to die. For some time after that, he stayed in his lair, rubbing his jaws against protuberances until the moth loosened and fell away.

That night, the big trout left the pool and cruised upstream, where he felt the hunting might be better. He was passing a cattail bed when a movement attracted his attention. A water vole, looking like a half-grown short-tailed rat, was propelling itself rapidly among the stalks with its webbed hind feet. Quicker than thought, Zar rushed after it, seized the swimming rodent by its chest and forelegs, and swallowed it head first. He had to gulp several times before the struggling creature finally was engulfed.

Almost immediately, a hot pain shot through Zar's

stomach. He raced upstream and leaped into the air, but could feel no pull of a fish line. In a few seconds, the water rat's squirmings died down. The cutthroat put about and hurried back to the pool and his den. Nothing seemed to want to molest him, however, and the pain in his belly dulled as his digestive juices began to dissolve the vole.

A fish-blood taste was infiltrating the lair about him. Zar did not know it, but this came from a small wound in his own side where the dying water rat's sharp incisor teeth had bitten through from his stomach in a last convulsion of agony. For several hours after that, Zar felt no urge to feed.

The surface of the pool was turning gray with dawn when Zar slipped out of his lair like a wraith and rose toward the shallows beside the reed bed. With a sudden slash, he charged into the midst of mother teal and her brood and, with his back partly out of water, seized a duckling and took off. Behind him, a peaceful scene was changed to a clamoring shambles.

Back in deeper water, Zar swallowed his prey and swam slowly down the middle of his pool, glancing from side to side while other trout darted away. So taken was he with his own importance that he did not notice a long, dark form overtaking him.

Lutra the otter was on the hunt. Attracted by the slash and cry in the reeds, he barely missed a lifetime's chance to corner the big cutthroat trout in shallow water. Now, his eyes red with rage, he was driving full speed ahead. And here in the pool he could travel as fast as most trout.

Some telepathic force—some natural radar—must have sounded a warning to Zar. At the last possible instant he flashed aside—and savage teeth clipped a corner out of his tail. He fled down the pool's length at frantic speed— unbalanced ever so little by the severed fragment—and escaped into Mill Creek below. For here was the one enemy in the water he feared. Other fish he held in contempt, but Lutra was as ruthless as himself.

In the creek, Zar had a chance, because Lutra could not
dodge around obstacles quite as quickly as himself. Had
he stayed in the pool and raced back and forth, his end
would have been certain, for terror and the slight handicap
of his injured tail would have tired him. Now, with the
single-minded drive of self-preservation, he shot downstream
between rocks and under logs. In moments, he had covered
the hundred yards between his pool and Mad River and
left Mill Creek.

With the fine edge of his speed gone, Zar was in no condition to carry on the sprint in Mad River's warmer water. He
fled into an accumulation of debris under flood control
pilings and worked his way deep into hiding. And it was
there Lutra gave up the chase, for men fished on those
piling posts, and he feared them more than the trout feared
him.

It was nearing sunrise next morning before the big cutthroat, attracted by Mill Creek's colder flow, found his way
back into the mouth of his native stream. Even then he was
nervous, and made a number of false starts. Finally, at day-
break, he took courage. One sprint and he was back in his
lair in the cool, familiar depths of Mill Creek pool.

Reaction set in. Zar was hungry. He had not eaten in
Mad River. So when a bird alighted on a bent reed and
leaned down to drink, he flashed to the surface and leaped,
open-jawed. But the bird's reflexes were finely keyed, and
it rocketed into the air, chattering with fear.

Zar landed with a splash like a salmon leap, spat out
several feathers, and drove fifty feet ahead in a rage. A
group of young trout scattered in panic, but too late for
one hapless six-incher. Zar swung back, still champing,
spied a young bullhead, and crushed it in his powerful
jaws. The prick of its spines recalled the feel of a hook. He
disappeared into the depths of the pool, and came to rest
in his lair, satisfied for the moment.

Gradually, as the day warmed, the pool settled back to

its normal tenor of watchfulness. But mother teal and her remaining brood had left it for other parts.

It landed on the surface above Zar's lair with a tiny plop —a mouse! The giant slipped out of his shelter and rose with a graceful sweep. But before he opened his jaws, a note of warning sounded within him. That mouse was false —like certain flies he had encountered. He veered away, and his tail churned water as he headed back to his den. Nor would he rise again, although a number of irritating, flashing things yawed back and forth in the pool to tempt other and less wary trout during the day.

It was nearing sundown when a mouse fell from a tree overhead. There was no mistaking this one. It was swimming frantically toward shore. Zar's breakfast was digested and forgotten. It was time to eat. What he could not see, as he rose open-mouthed, was a light line extending down from the tree to a hook which was tied onto the mouse's back like a pack load on a horse.

Zar swallowed the mouse head first—nor was he aware of any resistance until the little creature was halfway down his throat. Then the mouse pulled back with unexpected strength, and something bit sharply into the back of Zar's mouth. Alarmed, he attempted to spit out his prey. But not until he tried to sound deep into the pool—only to have his head jerked up with springy but positive strength—did he realize what had happened.

With an outraged rush, Zar was off. He burst out of the water like a speckled explosion, and raced the pool's length. So great was his speed that a slight bulge followed him atop the water.

Around he swung, and back, this time trying to reach his refuge with the single-minded purpose of a charging bull. Deep into his lair among the roots he drove—but the mouse still hung on and bit into the roof of his mouth.

He was lashing his head back and forth when a tremendous splash overhead startled him. Then, for the first

time in the battle, Zar felt fear. A large, dark form was
churning the water above, and extensions of it seemed to
be reaching down toward him.

The big trout backed out of his den and fled to the
head of the pool. What he could not see was that a limb
of a tree had broken, precipitating an excited angler into
the water. All he knew was that this enemy was larger
than any otter, and therefore more dangerous.

And now, with disruption of his system of defense, Zar
knew he was fighting for his life. He no longer felt angrily
sure of himself, but expended his strength against a resistance that pulled with supple and steady purpose toward
the place where the enemy had attacked. Nor would the big
trout try for his refuge again, for in the water above it, a
broken limb dangled menacingly.

Under the onset of fear—instead of rage, as in the past—
Zar lost his poise. And his nervous system was still on edge
from yesterday's encounter with Lutra. So his only impulse
was to stampede like his excitable relative, the rainbow
trout.

That broken limb had brought a new factor into the
conflict—one beyond Zar's capacity to surmount. Had the
limb not fallen, he would have ended the battle by returning to his lair as in the past, and tangling the leader about
the willow roots. Now he was exposed—smoked out—and he
did not know what to do about it.

For fifteen minutes, the tussle raged up and down the
pool, while other trout sought shelter or dashed about in
excitement. For equity was overturned—the monarch was
in jeopardy. Several times, Zar tried to leave the pool and
go downstream again, as he had done when fleeing from
Lutra. But a stout leader and supple rod in the hands of a
capable angler kept him within bounds.

A tiredness was coming over the powerful cutthroat, a
condition abetted by the wound in his tail. The strength
and vitality he had taken from other creatures for so long

were being burned up, while the foe he was fighting seemed as fresh as ever. More and more it became an ordeal to run the length of his pool. Always he had to fight that resistance, and drag it with him, instead of racing free.

Toward the end, he began to roll groggily and no longer was able to push down into deeper water. A kingfisher dived at him with insulting clatter as he churned the surface. A group of small trout parted to let him through their ranks, but none fled in terror now.

For the regency of Zar was tottering, and already word had spread with mysterious speed up and down Mill Creek. It came to mother teal, a quarter mile away, and she twittered assurance to her surviving broodlings. Even the gape-mouthed bullheads, whose bellies were always empty, sensed the change in a dim way.

At the last, Zar allowed himself to be towed toward the bank, floating on his side, while his broad tail whacked the surface in protest. And then his cold-pan eyes made out the enemy reaching for him from shore.

With one blast of wrath, the big trout's strength returned. Deep down into the pool he bored, while smaller trout scattered in panic. The kingfisher that had been clacking overhead flew away in silence. Furiously, Zar drove ahead faster than at any time since he had been hooked. No longer was he afraid. He raced up into the creek at the head of his pool and slashed his way into a tangle of water grasses.

And there the reserve strength that had flared so lustily burned out. Zar lay supine, gasping. And when the pull began to inch him out of his hideaway, he only flapped a tired tail. Out into the current again, he let himself be maneuvered down into the pool without a struggle.

The feel of deeper water penetrated the torpor of Zar's being. He winnowed sidewise against the quickening pull and brought up against a submerged clump of branches from a waterlogged tree. He floundered along the edge of this obstacle—and came to a stop. Ahead of him, the line twitched and jerked to free itself from the entanglement.

Unwittingly, Zar had accomplished what he had always done before in the root jungle of his lair. But he was too exhausted to realize what had happened. The killer trout had given up.

It was there, in the mists of the next day's dawn, that Lutra the otter found him, alive but dying from the hook in the roof of his mouth that had worked into the base of his brain as he struggled.

The angler had gone away, leaving considerable line draped about the submerged snag. But a strong leader, well tangled with flexible branches, had held. Zar never would have been able to free himself.

And so the teeth that severed his spinal cord to extinguish the final flicker accomplished a deed more kind than not.

Sun rays slanted through the clearing mists over Mill Creek pool. In the waters beneath, bullheads and small trout squabbled over the last shreds of tasty flesh about the submerged tangle. In the brightening day, mother teal and her little ones returned to their home among the reeds. Downstream in his den, Lutra slept.

Zar the destroyer, terror of the pool, was gone. Peace lay over the water.

The Outlaw of Mad River

From the Low Gap of Mad River down to its Big Bend is perhaps twenty-five miles as the stream falls. The region is a timbered wilderness, a stronghold primeval, locked in the fastness of the Redwood Empire mountains. A few animal trails traverse it as best they may, but even these give up where Mad River plunges down the wildest and most remote of its gorges, below Pilot Creek mouth.

It was here that Fel, the outlaw cougar or mountain lion, had his lair. Long ago, one of his forebears had discovered a cave deep in a fissure in the rock wall of Mad River gorge. And, as generations came and went, that cave was inherited by the regional cougar tribe's largest and most formidable male. Thus it now belonged to Fel, whose reputation as a killer was gaining note.

In the gorge below Pilot Creek mouth, Mad River climaxes its name. Ten-pound trout hole up in that fighting water. Deer, wild pigs, bear, and sundry big cats live in the forests and canyons tributary to the stream, isolated in measure from the onslaught of mankind. Ranch and logging roads never have penetrated that area and perhaps never will. It stands much as Indian lore remembers it, from unreckoned centuries ago.

Fel's days in the Mad River wilderness had been good. Here was his heritage, his domain, and he had grown to unusual size. Now, in his prime, he weighed a flush one hundred and eighty pounds—eight feet of tawny grace and power from nose to tail tip. King of his mountain fastness he was—king and its salient outlaw.

Aquamarine shadows had risen from the gorge below, and were creeping up the fir timber on the mountainside when Fel emerged from the deep split that led down to his lair. He did not come out at once, but watched from the shelter of an overhang for several minutes. Whether caution or the possibility of spotting prey prompted him to do this, only Fel knew, since mankind rarely came near his retreat. Finally he leapt atop a great boulder that was still warm from the summer sun and flexed every muscle of his body with meticulous care. He inhaled the cooling air of near-dusk, and savored of its odors. There would be good hunting this night, for the moon was nearly full.

But Fel was restless with that dissatisfaction which is born of excessive strength and well-being. Although he could have had all the best of it within a few miles of his lair, his range had expanded over a sweep some thirty miles in length, and fifteen miles wide—with his Mad River gorge hideout as its approximate center. This spread of hunting ground had taken him beyond the bounds of his wilderness beat and into the ranch holdings, both upstream at Low Gap and downstream at the Big Bend. And so he had come to learn that men, with their dogs and guns, knew of him and were his enemies.

This evening, Fel was not concerned with foes. The sweetish taste of young horseflesh lingered in his mouth and memory, and he wanted more. That the trip to get this delicacy meant both danger and absence from the daytime safety of his lair meant ever less as his desire increased. In fact, the day then drawing to a close was the first he had spent in the gorge cave since he had gone for a raid down in the Big Bend country, two nights before. And now he was leaving again—this time for the Low Gap, since it was closer and he felt that a change was needed. Men and dogs were becoming too watchful elsewhere.

As silently as the flight of an owl, the lithe mountain lion slipped through the dusk, stopping once at a spring to

drink and leave his scent. This last was for the information
of any female cougar that might be in season—in which
event the lioness would wait patiently at the scent place
for his return, since their species, like the domestic cat,
procreates at any season of the year. Having left notice
of availability, Fel continued on.

Fel's pace was not swift. Rather, he traveled at a steady,
easy glide, with almost no bouncing up and down—a gait
mastered long ago by the Indians, who can follow a trail
without rest for hours. By midevening, Fel was approaching the pastures and barns of Low Gap ranch. He had not
stopped for so much as a rabbit, and twice he had ignored
fresh deer tracks. Hunger was upon him, and his small
stomach ached—but his taste buds craved the satisfaction
of young horses' blood. His eyes glowed pale with anticipa-
tion as the odor of colt was wafted downcanyon by the
cool air that followed the river.

He leaped a barbed-wire fence with the grace of a stag,
since he had come to scorn mankind's barricades long ago.
Then he glided along a line of trees toward the main
corrals. The odor of prey was heavy in the air now, but
none seemed about. Presently he came to a sandy swale
where he had covered over his last victim from the Low
Gap herd, several nights before. An emanation of putrid
flesh hung over the depression, but it was not the smell of
colt. A buzzard had come down to feed upon the carrion
of Fel's kill and had been caught in a steel trap meant
for the returning killer. Maggots were into the bird's remains, and the air was foul. Fel turned away in disgust.
Later, when his tracks were seen to change course just
outside the circle of traps, he got credit for rather more
sagacity than he possessed.

But no mares with their young were in sight, although a
few older horses were on a nearby hillside. These did not
interest Fel. He wanted more tender meat than theirs. The
air was redolent with the nearness of colts, but the odor-

trail led to the barns, not far from a group of men's dwellings. And Fel, despite his increasing boldness, never had
gone close to any human being's habitation. These harbored
a threat of the unknown—and there were always dogs about.

A fifteen minutes' circuit of the surroundings revealed
that all the young horses seemed to have hidden in the
barns. Baffled, Fel paused and looked about. The older
horses on the hillside had disappeared, and once a dog
had barked. It was then that he caught a fresh and tempting
odor from upwind and decided to follow it to its source.

Another mile took him to a small, high-fenced corral,
somewhat removed from a house. In this enclosure he
found what he wanted—a golden-coated Palomino colt with
its dam. The mare snorted in terror when she saw a huge,
pale-eyed apparition glide from the brush toward the fence.
She galloped to the far end of the corral, herding her
youngster ahead, whereupon Fel made his decision. He
cleared the six-foot barrier as easily as he would hurdle a
line fence—and came face-to-face with the fury of mother
love.

Straight for him charged the mare, striking with her
forefeet and screaming. Fel dodged aside as lightly as a
professional boxer would side-step an amateur's rush. Then,
even as he had killed deer without number in the past, he
sprang onto the mare's shoulders and buried his fangs
deep into her neck, behind the ears. At the same time, his
murderous hind claws began tearing her flanks. Maddened
with pain and wounded to the death, the mare crashed
through the fence and collapsed on her side, moaning.

Fel bounced clear of the dying dam—and there the ranch
dog caught up with him. The dog was big and enraged.
The defense of his home premise was at stake. Roaring at
the top of his voice, he flung himself at the outlaw. Seconds
later, the dog lay writhing on the ground, disemboweled
by one fearful slash.

Leaving his attacker to cry its life out, Fel whipped back

into the corral and dispatched the trembling colt. Then, disdaining the break in the fence, he picked up his victim and cleared the barrier as easily as he had come in. A dozen leaps took him to the first brush, and he headed downslope toward the river. A few drops of blood were showing on his neck, where the dog had gotten in one chop, but he was scarcely aware of it. Back in the house, a terrified woman was cranking a telephone in a vain effort to reach her husband before the marauder left.

Fel did not travel far. The exertion of making three kills in quick succession, together with the weight he was carrying, soon overtaxed that weakness which is Nature's check upon his species—bobcat-sized lungs and a heart no larger than an egg. He stopped at the river's edge, gasping, and for several minutes was unable to feed. Then, as his heart and lungs slowed down, he began his meal. In a short time Fel was satisfied, since his limited stomach capacity could handle no more than a half-dozen pounds of meat at a time.

Fel was in no hurry now. He licked himself clean, then pulled the remains of his prey onto a sand bar, where he dug a shallow bed and covered it with brush and scrapings. He had finished and started to drink, when he became aware of the sound of a truck driving at high speed on the road above, approaching the scene of his recent raid.

The outlaw cougar had no way of connecting cause and effect in a matter like this, but something about that vehicle's haste seemed directed toward him. He heard it clatter into the yard beside the house, while men's voices mingled with the yelping of dogs to upset the quiet of a moonlit mountain night. There was no mistaking it now— the enemies were rushing toward the corral and river. He spat in the direction of the uproar and started downstream along the bank.

He had rounded a turn of the river, perhaps two hundred yards away, when he heard the pack arrive at the stream and redouble their noise as they discovered the kill. That was enough. At once, Fel plunged into Mad River, crossed it in a dozen strokes, and cut through a wooded peninsula to the next bend of the stream. He had discovered early in life that water was one of the best ways to foil pursuit. Nor was his action unusual, for mountain lions seem to have no aversion to water and will swim fair-sized streams if hard pressed.

Although Fel did not possess that keen sense of strategy which characterizes the canine tribes, he was a cougar of more than average acumen. As such, he had perception enough to realize that one trick, worked consistently, produced results. In the next hour, he crossed Mad River a number of times and finally swam through a small gorge, before taking to the woods. Nighttime favored him as well, and when he decided, toward morning, to double back to the cache of his kill, all was quiet.

It was here the men made a mistake. Had they taken time to set traps around the remains of Fel's prey, they might have ended the killer's career that night. But they had had a hot trail, and when they lost it at the small gorge, no one thought of doing anything more until daylight. And so Fel feasted again and took to the fir forests a couple of miles downstream to spend the day—which was where the outlaw of Mad River likewise made a mistake.

Fel's kill that night had been no ordinary one. The Palominos belonged to a weathy visitor who swore vengeance. And so old Bert the lion tracker was brought in at once by plane. Bert was a small, quiet-spoken man, who wore bifocal glasses and understood mountain lions. Likewise, he suspected that this was the same cougar that had caused trouble in the Big Bend country below. Rewards were being offered from there by now, which further interested Bert. By midmorning he and his dogs were on Fel's trail.

At first, Fel was only annoyed. He wanted to sleep and

had selected a shady glen at the head of a draw for that purpose. But there was no mistaking the sounds starting up the draw, a half-mile below. He left his shelter and climbed almost to the top of a nearby ridge, where he stopped to reconnoiter. Below him was Mad River's canyon, which he could reach by crossing the ridge and going down an adjoining draw that led back to the water's edge. On the mountainside behind him were fir forests extending for miles across the coastal range, until they met the redwoods down by the sea.

By now the day had turned warm, and the river below offered both safety by water and coolness. After a quick glance in all directions, Fel slipped over the ridge and sought the shelter of its lee side. Then he started down the adjoining draw for Mad River.

Fel's plan was well conceived, and he would have gained a mile over the pursuit, had it not been for one shrewd dog in Bert's pack. Big Scotty, like Bert, was wise in the lore of cougars. So when Scotty abruptly turned back toward the river, Bert decided not to push farther up the draw until something developed.

By now, Fel's decision was made. There was an ominousness in the air that warned him that this was no ordinary pursuit. As soon as he reached the river, he would head downstream until he reached his lair, deep in the gorge below Pilot Creek mouth. It would be a long trip, and his eyes glinted greenish with rage at this intrusion upon his sleep period. But safety lay in his distant hideout, and it was there he wanted to be.

Fel did not even pause to look when he emerged onto the river bank from the draw, so certain he was that the man and his dogs had not even crossed the ridge above and started down again. And there he all but ran headlong into Big Scotty!

Instantly the canyon was a bedlam of noise. Fel snarled in startled outrage and plunged into the stream, with Scotty roaring after him. Up in the first draw, Bert sprang to his feet, fired his gun to rally the pack, and hurried back toward the river.

The Mad River wilderness is a rugged terrain, and Bert lost a precious minute struggling through underbrush and over large rocks. He berated himself for not following Scotty before, but when he scrambled atop a boulder overlooking the stream, neither dog nor mountain lion was in sight.

At about this moment, Fel decided to cross the river again. His dun-colored flank showed briefly, some three hundred yards downstream, but that was enough. Something struck him a hot blow on one shoulder, and another bullet whanged off a rock beside his head. If Fel had been angry before, he was maddened now. In back of him, the pack was howling in full cry as the dogs raced toward the sound of Bert's gun. Close behind him was Big Scotty, determined and grim, and no longer wasting energy on noise. His shoulder felt numb. Blood was running down one foreleg. He was still able to travel, but the odds were no longer in his favor.

Down the canyon went the big cougar at a fast lope, clearing small boulders and dodging through undergrowth seemingly without effort. But his shoulder was hard hit, and the excitement and pain were telling upon his strength. Before long, his undersized lungs were pumping in agony, and his heart drumming. In his consciousness one factor drove him ahead with single intent—the desire to reach the security of his lair, still several miles away. Toward that end, his entire life force was concentrating itself.

As a result, the primal instinct exploded when he splashed into a riffle to cross the river—and found that Big Scotty had made a detour and overtaken him. Fel swung about in belly-deep water, and delivered a frightful rake full into the face of his pursuer. Torn and blinded, Scotty groped ashore and floundered into the brush.

Something in that encounter seemed to stimulate the mountain lion's adrenals. He felt a returning surge of

strength rise through his body as its bloodstream rushed
fresh oxygen into every cell. He glided on his way at once,
and kept up an even pace for some time, crossing the river
frequently. But behind him, ever closer, came the clamor
of the pack. Once it had risen to frenzied heights when
the stricken Scotty was discovered. And his shoulder was
hurting him more with every stride; nor could he, in common with most cats, stand pain well. Blood flecked along
his flank, taking toll from his vitality and endurance with
every drop lost.

A half hour passed, and Fel was nearing the end of his
strength. Now, although his every instinct warned against
the weakness that wanted it, he was about to take to a tree.
The pack was less than a hundred yards behind and would
have overtaken him before this had he not crossed the
river so often. Even so, they had come into sight a time
or two, and their cries were blood-hungry.

At this critical juncture, Fel reached the spring where
he had stopped to drink the night before—and where he
had left his scent. A female cougar was waiting there,
seemingly chained to the spot by the secondary instinct.
She ran up to Fel, but he repulsed her with a snarl and
dodged aside. The lioness was as aware of the oncoming
pack as Fel, but she was neither hurt nor tired, and her
eagerness cost him several seconds of his fast dwindling
lead. Then the first dog appeared upon the scene.

Fel leaped for the river and plunged across. But the
lioness stood transfixed for a moment, apparently unable to
tear herself away. The pack rushed at her in full cry. She
wheeled back into the forest and almost immediately
climbed a tree.

The respite from that lioness saved Fel. Once again he
crossed Mad River, and when he reached the flank of the
gorge, he scaled its side toward the split that led into his
hideout. A half mile behind, he could hear the dogs baying
beneath their treed quarry. Fel paused momentarily to

make certain that none was on his trail. Then he slipped down the fissure and into the darkness of his lair.

Bert arrived at the spring angry and disgusted. This was not the cougar he wanted; it was smaller and not even wet from swimming the river. He thought bitterly of Big Scotty back there with a merciful bullet through his head. He had loved that dog—nor would Scotty have let himself be lured off trail by any decoy. He hung the lioness' carcass in the fork of a tree, summoned the pack, and started downstream toward Mad River gorge.

A quiet hour passed before the arriving yells of Bert's dogs hit Fel's ears down in the fissure. He stopped licking his wound and listened. Never before had a dog pack reached this place. Even so, he felt secure. No dog could worm its way down and have room to attack. He could kill them one at a time as they arrived, and let the carcasses drop into the rapids, far below. He spat as the yammering increased.

But Fel reckoned without the man—a creature hampered by a slow and clumsy body, but who had a superior brain.

For some time, Bert studied the situation. He leaned far over the abyss and noted that the fissure gaped over the torrent below. He even lowered himself part way down the split and got a general idea of the lair's location. Then he began to cut wood and brush. . . .

Fel knew there was a fire somewhere about, from the faint fumes that trickled down into his lair. But he was totally unprepared for the conflagration that tumbled down into the fissure. Bert had done his work well. He had built a bonfire atop the overhang. Then, when it reached the peak of its blaze, he tilted the flaming mass into the split, using a pole branch as a lever. In moments, Fel was strangling.

The trapped mountain lion backed into the farthest corner of his den. Smoke poured in like a deluge, stinging his lungs and blinding his eyes. His consciousness was slipping when the primal instinct again asserted itself. Desperately, and only half aware of what he was doing, Fel charged through the smoldering embers toward the nearest fresh air. That air was sucking upward from the fissure's opening that overlooked the rapids, drawing smoke past his lair and discharging it at the entrance atop the cliff, where the man and his dogs waited.

Fel got his first draught of smoke-free air when he stuck his head out of the opening, high above the raging river. He was retching, but his eyes began to clear. And, as his vision returned, he looked up and saw a man trying to aim a gun at him from above.

Had Bert had a rope to secure himself, he could have shot the outlaw without further trouble. But the nearest rope was at Low Gap ranch, ten miles away. And so perilous was the slope to which he clung, face down, that he gave up after all but slipping off into Mad River's rock-torn water—and death—below. Sweating and holding with finger-nails that bled, he wormed his way back to safety, and started again to cut firewood—this time in greater quantity.

Fel was still by the riverside opening of the fissure when a burning deluge crashed over and around him. In an instant, the split was an inferno of fire and smoke. No flesh could stand that. He yowled and leaped into space, his great body twisting and turning in an effort to land feet first in the rapids that raced up to meet him.

The first two shots tore through Fel before he struck the white-crested water. More hit his battered body as it swirled downstream and went under.

For several minutes old Bert stood on a pinnacle, eyes shaded, and looked down into the turmoil of Mad River gorge. Then he shook his head and turned away. It was getting late. He was tired. And there was nothing more he could do. They would have to take his word for it. . . .

Wings Regained

When Tohwah, the whistling swan, and his mate, the pen, reached the coast of northern California early in November, they felt that their southward migration was finished. A dozen pairs of the great white birds had left their nesting grounds in Alaska, north of the Arctic circle, after a late October sun had sunk so low on the horizon that shore ice was thickening day and night.

Led by its oldest male, or "cob," with Tohwah relieving now and then, the V-shaped phalanx of swans followed the Pacific coast down from the north along the shores of British Columbia, Washington, and Oregon. Despite an average wingspread of six feet, which could speed them up to seventy miles per hour if necessary, their trip had been a perilous one.

Lawbreaking hunters and wild animals had harassed them when they stopped, eagles attacked them on the wing, while airplanes filled them with dread. Several of their number had been shot, a pair of eagles had knocked down and killed two more, but the rest arrived at journey's end in safety.

Now they were scattered along the coastal lagoons and stream mouths of the Redwood Empire, in an abundant land that never froze. Here they would spend the winter and build up reserves for their return flight to the Arctic in spring.

Tohwah and Pen chose a secluded pond near Widow White Creek mouth in Humboldt County, where a concrete dam, erected long ago, impounded several acres of water.

Sections of this pond had been seeded to food grasses by a conservation-minded owner who lived in a lumber town some distance away. Fir, alder, and willow coverts shut in much of it, and beavers lived there, while deep reed banks along the shore made the place an ideal retreat. What Tohwah and Pen had yet to learn was that the pond's owner occasionally invited friends there to shoot.

The pair of swans were pleased with their new location. True, a logging railroad passed near by, and on the other side of this was a hunting cabin that belonged to the pond's owner. But these were well screened by trees, while the pond itself, with its succulent water snails and profuse food grasses, quite satisfied them. Also, there were numbers of good hiding places, as well as a small island in one bay of the pond, while the familiar rumble of the Pacific Ocean sounded assurance a quarter mile away.

At first, Tohwah and Pen were disturbed when the logging train made its twice daily trip past their haven. But they soon learned that it never approached the pond, and came to pay no more attention to it than did the several half-tame ducks who lived there all year. On the train, the swans were noticed by friendly eyes, but, in time, word would spread to others that were not friendly.

The swans selected an alder thicket intergrown with cattails and near the creek inlet for their roosting place. For the first two nights they slept undisturbed. On the third night, they were awakened by a feeling of danger that made every nerve tingle. For moments they heard nothing except the riffle of the stream as it flowed into the pond. Then came the slightest of movements, close by. A pause, and the sound was repeated—nearer this time.

High in a fir tree, a great horned owl's hoot boomed across the night. Out in the pond, a duck yeeped and was still. Tension heavy as a nightmare brooded over the scene, waiting to explode.

Suddenly Tohwah's mind was made up. With a crash and a flap, he and Pen burst free of their shelter toward the water. The instant they started, two furry forms leaped out of the darkness and landed atop them. With mad clamoring and beating of wings, the swans pushed into the water dragging their attackers—who tried to tear through their neck feathers and sever the life cord within.

But the outlaw dogs had taken on bigger game than they expected—some twenty pounds of swan apiece. In seconds, they were pulled into the water, where the swans had every advantage. Wings that could break a man's leg buffeted them until they wanted only to get away. They let go and plunged toward shore, hastened by hissing beaks that struck snakelike at their hindquarters, gouging out fur.

Tohwah and Pen retreated to the small island to nurse their hurts, while a bevy of ducks yammered in alarm. They had not chosen the island for a roost at first, because it had no thickets and only a sparse growth of cattails. Now it seemed a welcome refuge, and they never roosted ashore again.

The horned owl swung down from his watchtower on soundless wings, crossed the pond to inspect, and swooped upon a hare in an adjoining meadow. He bore it back to the tree, screaming of death, while every creature on the pond froze in silence.

Next morning, a man came to Widow White Creek pond. Tohwah and Pen got a glimpse of him as he approached from the railroad embankment, and took to the air. The man watched the broad-winged birds gain altitude and veer out toward the sea. He shook his head in regret, for he was the pond's owner, and the train crew had told him about the swans.

Later, he discovered tufts of drifting white feathers about the swans' roosting place and reconstructed the night's at-

tack. Bobcats or varmints of some kind—he thought—they'll
never come back now.

The man was a busy executive with a lumber company,
and rarely visited his pond during the week. Few others
came onto the premises, as he did not want it disturbed,
and his word carried weight. Thus there were days at a
time when Tohwah and Pen saw no evidence of mankind
except the logging train, and they became increasingly con-
tented with their haven. Often they made flights up and
down the coast to visit others of their flock, and would not
see the pond's owner when he stopped by. But night always found them back at their roost on the small island.
Food abounded everywhere, and they were regaining the
weight they had lost during their long flight from the Arctic.

It was past the middle of November, in the week that
duck season opened, that matters at the pond suddenly
changed. The swans had heard suspicious sounds ashore,
toward dawn one morning. But, since nothing tried to
molest them on their island, they did not fly.

Just before sunrise, several loud bangs shattered the new
day's calm, and wild ducks took wing, crying alarm.

Startled, Tohwah ran the length of the island with out-
spread wings and launched himself over the water and into
the air, with Pen following. He was putting all his strength
into the getaway, when a blast and a blow knocked him
into the water. Wild with fear, he tried to take off again,
but could not. One wing was useless.

Men called out, while Pen flew away, but no more shots
were fired. Faster than a canoe could travel, the big swan
paddled back to his island and hid in the cattails.

Figures rose out of the brush on shore. "Good Lord, I
though it was a goose!" a man's voice exclaimed.

Overhead, Pen circled anxiously in the growing light,
crying with that silver-fluted note which distinguishes the
whistler from its almost extinct relative, the trumpeter swan.

Then an even more terrifying thing happened to Tohwah.

Two men got into a boat and rowed across the water toward the island—the one place he and Pen had considered safe. When their direction became obvious, Tohwah backed out of the reeds and, beating his wings and paddling full speed, raced for the lower end of the pond. But the men in the boat did not follow.

"His wing isn't broken," said the owner. "You could tell from the way he flapped it. Looks as if only the tip is disabled."

The visitor who had done the shooting was downcast. "What a trigger-touched joker I am," he said. "But I never dreamed there'd be swans here."

"Of course not," said the owner. "I'm to blame for that. I forgot to mention them. In fact, I had only seen them a couple of times myself."

"Listen, Herb," said the visitor. "Why don't you close this place to any more shooting until that fellow heals up?"

"I will," said the owner. "We'll finish our morning's shoot, and then call it a job until mister whistler recovers. He'll leave this place fast enough after that."

But the appearance of the men had driven the wild ducks away. During the next hour, only a straggling few returned. Finally the hunters gave it up and went to the cabin for breakfast.

They had been out of sight perhaps a half hour when a white form materialized out of the sky, and Pen dropped down to the pond, crying anxiously. Tohwah came out of hiding at the lower end and headed back to the island with answering tremolos.

For several minutes, Pen flew back and forth over the Widow White marsh area at what would have been a fatally low level, had there been gunners about. Then she dropped onto the water with easy grace, legs folded instead of braced ahead like ducks and geese.

What may have passed between the pair of swans is denied the most sensitive devices of mankind to record.

Suffice to say that Pen took up unceasing watch over her disabled mate thereafter, sharing the misfortune that had struck him.

But no more hunters visited the pond now. In fact, no men came to it at all, although a man who walked back and forth along the railroad tracks at times worried the swans. What they had no way of knowing was that he was the logging railroad's right-of-way inspector, who had been asked by Herb to watch for trespassers.

Tohwah stayed on the island at all times now, venturing to shore for food only at dawn and sunset. Pen clucked and bustled about him, ready to sound the danger call at the slightest suspicion. At times, she would lay her neck on Tohwah's and croon to him with a soft "wow-wow-wowoo" that made the inspector rub his eyes in disbelief and debate whether to risk telling what he had seen or not.

Toward the week's end, Herb and the inspector held a conference at the cabin. "He flaps his wings," the inspector said, "but he can't seem to get traction. He's got a disabled wing tip, all right. Do you suppose we'd better catch him and look at it?"

The owner shook his head. "That'd just scare 'em to death, I'm afraid. Tell you what, Elmer—suppose I bring down a sack of corn kernels, and we'll take some out to the island every day. You do the job on weekdays, and I'll take care of it Saturdays and Sundays. If we feed him plenty, he ought to knit up faster. What d'you think?"

"It's a deal," approved the inspector.

That same day, Tohwah and Pen were thrown into panic by the appearance of the boat, and it was some time before Pen returned and the two of them dared approach the island again. There they found golden kernels scattered about, and began feeding at once.

Within a week, they had come to associate the boat with new and desirable food. Pen no longer flew away, but went to the end of the pond with her mate. Tohwah stopped trying to hide, and watched eagerly while Elmer or Herb spread the grain. Hardly would the man reach the railroad embankment before both swans were back on the island. But Tohwah's wing remained disabled.

Then one day Elmer noticed an intruder's tracks along the pond shore and at the boat landing. They were freshly made that morning, and there was evidence of shooting. Accordingly, he decided to stay overnight at the cabin, after telephoning Herb.

The swans also had seen a strange figure skulking about, gun in hand. Instinctively, they lay low in the rushes on the far side of their island; nor did Pen fly when the man shot a half-tame duck down by the dam.

The intruder had come from a nearby transient camp, attracted by rumors of big birds at Widow White Creek pond. He noted that someone had been feeding corn when he tried to break the lock on Herb's boat and decided to watch. It was then he saw the swans, and was not long in discovering that one of them appeared crippled. But the sun had risen by then, and he was afraid to shoot again.

Next morning, before dawn, the intruder was back again —this time with a snare and corn. He laid out a tempting golden heap on the shore nearest the island, set his snare, and went into hiding.

For some time, the two swans watched in suspicion. This was the first time food had been left on shore, instead of on the island. But the corn appeared harmless, and presently Tohwah ventured toward shore, where he had often foraged in the past. He paddled back and forth for a time, approaching nearer with each turn. Pen hung back, whistling querulous notes, but she was accustomed to the corn coming from men and could see no danger, despite the change in location.

Then Tohwah decided to act. He stepped ashore and commenced picking up the yellow kernels. Hardly had he gobbled down his first beakfull when something seized his ankles—and he was caught!

In vain he beat his wings and lunged at the intruder who sprang out of the brush. In vain Pen rushed at the man, to lose heart when he shouted and swung a club at her. A blow on the head stilled Tohwah, and the thief shoved him into a gunnysack.

He was running toward the railroad track when Elmer, armed with a pickaxe handle, stepped into his path.

"All right," he said quietly. "March ahead of me to the cabin. And remember—I won't need much excuse to knock your head off."

They reached the cabin in silence. Elmer picked up the phone. In the sack, where he had been dropped to the floor, Tohwah quivered ever so slightly.

By the time Herb arrived with a game warden, Tohwah, who had been taken out of the sack, was showing faint signs of life. Elmer and the warden examined him, while Herb guarded the prisoner.

"He should come out of it," the warden said. "But it's a wonder that blow didn't kill him instantly."

Elmer was looking at Tohwah's crippled wing. "It's lucky he was caught, all right," he said. "This wing tip needs to be wired into place before it can knit properly."

"O.K.," said Herb. "We'll take him to a veterinary."

"We don't need to," said the inspector. "I worked for a vet in my younger days, and haven't forgotten. We have a first-aid kit right here, and some light leader wire. It'll be easy to take care of him while he's still groggy."

A half hour later, with his broken wing tip skillfully wired into place, Tohwah was carried to the pond and released. Overhead, a frightened Pen circled high and watched. The men gave the big swan a gentle push, and instinct prompted him to paddle toward the island. But it was obvious that he was a sick bird.

"That's about all we can do," Elmer said. "Let's get out of here so his mate will come back."

It was several days before Tohwah's head began to clear from the blow that had all but opened his skull. Pen would not leave his side as he drooped in a daze—although at first, when the boat came with food, she wanted desperately to fly away.

Slowly, Tohwah began to recover. And as his appetite returned, his awareness of self came back. At first, Pen tried to remove the tiny wires that secured his wing tip, but it would be some time before these would rust away and fall off. Before long, the swans came to regard them as part of Tohwah's regular equipment and, since they caused no trouble, forgot them.

One day, in the midst of a December downpour, Tohwah decided to fly. Urged by Pen's fluting contralto alongside, he made a run down the pond, beating his wings and paddling with all his strength—and rose from the water!

He circled the little island beside his mate, only to have to land again as his wing weakened. But it was a start, and during the afternoon, when the storm had slackened, he tried flight again. This time Elmer saw him from the railroad tracks and hastened to the phone, while the swans rubbed necks and crooned happily.

Herb arrived promptly, but for some time thereafter the two men stood on the railroad embankment and watched, while an icy drizzle trickled down their necks and seeped into their clothes.

"Of course, I might make 'em fly," Elmer observed, grinning.

"Over my dead body," said Herb. "Or yours, if they don't, you donkey doctor!"

About then, the logging train hove into sight on its return trip, and the engineer blew a staccato greeting. That did it, for the train almost never whistled in that secluded area.

Into the air went both swans, to circle over the entire pond before Tohwah came down.

"'Twas worth it," Herb said. "You've made history, Elmer."

Progress was slow, however, and it was late January before Tohwah and Pen left the shelter of Widow White Creek pond and tried a run over the ocean. Thereafter Tohwah gained confidence as the mending wing tip gained strength, and the faithful Pen felt an upsurge of assurance after her long vigil.

It was about that time that Pen began to lead Tohwah as they flew over a widening radius—a thing she never had done before. Her reasons were sound. The cob who led their flock was passing his prime. And when the change in command came, Tohwah would take over. So Tohwah must be ready when the call came to go north, early in March.

A few Sundays later, when the first feel of spring was in the air, a congenial group of friends met at the cabin. Interested guests were escorted along the railroad embankment to look through the trees at the swans.

"There's a change coming," inspector Elmer said to his wife. "I've felt it for a couple of days, but the swans have known it longer than that."

"Do you think they'll go away before long?" she asked.

"Fairly soon, I think. They've been doing a lot of neck craning and gabbling lately. And the old man can fly about as far as he wants, now. Talk about devotion—the way his mate stood by him was wonderful to see."

Perhaps it was the chattering and laughter that came from the area of the cabin. Perhaps Tohwah and Pen felt the time had come to reconnoiter. No one could know. But that afternoon the men and their families witnessed a splendid sight.

Calling in flutelike accord, Tohwah and Pen rose from the pond with translucent-winged strokes silhouetted against a lowering sun at sea. Higher and higher into the blue they mounted, while a fascinated group watched from the cabin yard. Once, the sun's rays made them reflect a shell-like pink as they banked below piled-up clouds. And then they were gone into space, while their elfin-bugle notes still echoed in the sensibilities of the watchers.

"Thus endeth the story," Herb said.

"I'm not too sure," said Elmer.

Three days passed, but the pair of swans did not return to Widow White Creek pond. Although Elmer felt it was not quite time for them to start north, he began to give up hope. He continued to set out food as always, but the mud hens and ducks appropriated it, now that the island was no longer occupied.

At sundown of the third day, after Elmer had gone by for the last time, Tohwah and Pen returned to their island. Corn had been spread late that afternoon, and some of it remained, which they ate hungrily. Tohwah's wing was as strong as ever now, and they settled for the night with cheerful chatter and ado.

They had flown up and down the coast, visiting members of their group, to pass the word that Tohwah was healed. And when the great white birds returned to their nesting grounds along the Arctic Sea, he would be ready to go—and take command when the time came. All was right with their world again.

It was there Elmer found them, while on his early inspection run. Although this was not the regular feeding time, he filled a measure of corn and got into the boat. Tohwah and Pen watched him with interest and did not leave the island until he was halfway out to it. Then they paddled about in the middle of the pond, eyeing the familiar man and boat and giving an occasional chuckle which to Elmer sounded like a greeting between old friends.

Before the inspector had moored the boat ashore, the swans were back on the island at feed. For some time the man watched, pleased as he rarely had been. Then he went to the cabin and phoned Herb.

"They've come back!" he exulted. "And my money says they'll be with us every winter, after this. They belong to the family now."

The Promised Land

Pollux the beaver and his mate Polly spent the year 1939 as guests of the San Francisco Exposition. They were one of three pairs that had been sent from Canada for the occasion. At first, the beavers were not supplied with "gnawing wood," and their incisor teeth had grown to such lengths that they had been all but unable to open their mouths, and one of their number died from inability to feed.

About that time, a lumberman from the redwood region noticed the beavers' plight and sent a truckload of small logs for use in whittling their teeth down to normal length. That accomplished, they soon felt at home and became as nonchalant as fry cooks in a restaurant window.

Now, however, a change was in the air. Visitors had stopped lining their pond's fence, and Pollux and his cohorts missed them and felt restless. But the lumberman who had saved their lives earlier in the year had not forgotten and was back in San Francisco to make a deal.

It was felt that beavers would prosper in California's well-watered northern Redwood Empire—in fact, Nature had designed that domain for beavers. That none was there was an oversight which could be remedied by taking the animals in question and "planting" them in this propitious land.

The Exposition authorities had many matters on their minds. Of minor importance was the disposal of the five beavers, now that the show was done. So Pollux and company were put in crates and loaded onto a truck. After a lengthy trip, they were removed from that vehicle and transferred to a railway speeder. By now, there were odors of promise in the air, and their noses were aquiver.

Up into the coast range mountains, over a discontinued logging railroad chugged the speeder, at times crawling over trestles that were beginning to sag. Finally they stopped. Although the beavers disliked the confinement of their metal-lined traveling boxes, they were not unduly disturbed. So much had happened since they left their native land a year ago, that they were inured to change, people, and noise.

The lumberman was delighted. "First beavers among the redwoods," he said to his associate. "I hope they'll take. Easy now with the pinch bars, so we won't scare them."

Moments later, Pollux stood on the bank of the abandoned Camp 20 swimming hole, on Little River. There was a woodsy tang about him, while mountain water foamed a symphony of freedom and the out-of-doors. It had been a long time since he last had heard that. Nearby were alder, poplar, and willow thickets, while timbered hills loomed close by. Memories from a thousand generations stirred him. This was what he wanted.

Polly ran down to the shore and joined him; but hers was the more practical viewpoint. She began at once to wash her face and paws, while the other three beavers, one at a time, arrived beside her. Cleansing done, the four of them plunged into the pool.

But Pollux took his time, washing and preening himself in the cool, clear water. He looked back at the two men, standing on the railroad embankment, took a deep breath, and found it good.

"All right young fellow, it's all yours—and may your tribe increase," the lumberman said, laughing.

And with that, Pollux slid into the water to join his mate. Gone were his associations with mankind. Here was the lost abode again—but a different abode, and closer to human beings than his native homeland.

Scarcely had the men gone away before all the beavers were out of water again. They were hungry, and here was a land untouched by their species. Roots, grasses, bulbs, as well as toothsome varieties of bark, were abundant everywhere. In the late fall evening they gorged to satiety. The two mated pairs stayed together at first, but the remaining widowed or "odd" beaver went away by himself and was not seen again.

Before morning, the couples had separated, and Pollux and Polly started downstream to locate a place that would shelter them from the coming winter. Instinct warned them that preparations must be made at once—but what instinct could not tell them was that this was a land where snow almost never fell and the stream never froze.

In a bowl-like mountain meadow, a half mile below the onetime logging camp, the pair of beavers found the location they wanted. Here, Pollux' preliminary survey told him, a dam could be built where a tributary stream flowed into Little River. Before night was over, he was at work cutting alders to the exact length wanted and laying them out where he planned a dam to shelter their lodge and food larder. Polly worked beside him—and it was here that danger first struck.

Pollux was several yards away from the stream, about to start work on a young poplar, when he found his return blocked by a savage-appearing animal fully his own size but longer-legged.

Now Pollux and Polly knew what bobcats were, but this bobcat never had seen a beaver before. It stared in surprise, while Pollux grated his teeth and humped menacingly. To the bobcat, here was a creature that smelled like food but was unexpectedly large. Just how dangerous it could be was unknown. The cat sniffed the air and advanced a step. Pollux hissed and lunged.

The cat paused, and matters reached a deadlock. Out in the stream, Polly hit the surface a resounding whack with her broad tail. The cat jumped and wheeled toward the sound—and Pollux raced for the water.

That was all the bobcat needed to learn. This strange animal was afraid. It leapt after Pollux, raked a clawful of fur from his back, and seized his tail. Quick as a knife flash, a set of powerful incisor teeth sliced one of the cat's forelegs. It let go with a scream and sprang back into the brush.

Pollux was frightened and bleeding, but not badly hurt. For some time, he and Polly stayed in a nearby pool on watch. Thus the pair of beavers relearned a lesson in the new land—a lesson they had tended to forget during their year in San Francisco—that enemies were everywhere and the price of survival was unceasing vigilance. Thereafter, very little escaped their notice.

What is it that tells the beaver the proper way to calculate his stream stress, the proper way to reeve his interlocking work to make it watertight, and where best to allow for overflow? Mankind, with his beginnings of comprehension, is satisfied to call it instinct—but there are many who question further . . . for how else could it have come to be? How else could all living creatures have been taught? The Divine mystery of creation cares for us all, if we but realized.

Within a week, the beavers had built a stout dam across the tributary stream near where it joined Little River at the foot of its meadow and were at work on their lodge. Inborn knowledge told them that Little River itself was too large to dam, but what their knowledge could not foresee was that Little River's watershed had been logged off and that the heavy rains of winter, with no snowfall to check, could cause severe floods. And so, Pollux and Polly felt they had the situation on the tributary well under control.

There are types of human beings who will murder senselessly if given a chance. With such as these in mind, the lumberman had tried to keep the release of the beavers in Little River a secret. But in time, word got about in the lumber town beside lower Little River, near the sea. To most of the townspeople, the news was interesting, and they no more wanted to kill the newcomers than to burn the forests.

One ferret-eyed man, however, felt differently. Before long, he had the pelt of the "odd" beaver in his cabin and was openly looking for more. At this point, one of his neighbors lost patience and reported the matter to the local game warden. Caught with the evidence, the lawbreaker was hailed before a justice court, fined, and, when he could not pay, sent to jail.

Winter rains had started soon after Pollux and Polly were set free. But now, while Ferret-eyes was languishing in jail, disaster struck. A January storm poured rain steadily for a week, and the streams rose to torrents. In a colder climate, much of this rain would have been snow. Here, on the comparatively warm coast of northern California, the run-off went berserk.

For two days, Pollux and Polly labored in desperation to save their possessions. But on the third night, their dam went out, and with it their lodge and winter's store of food. Loss of the food meant little, since it was obtainable the year round. But to the beavers, descended from an ancestry that knew only a stern climate, it was a disaster of magnitude.

On the fourth day, Little River's muddy flood overflowed its banks, and even their tributary stream was unrecognizable. The two beavers were without shelter, enemies were on the prowl, and their only protection lay in the rushing, angry water. Downstream with it they went and, within a mile of the lumber town, found and took over a den that was high and dry. Here they stayed out the flood.

Who can say a wild creature is only a "mechanical toy," run by instinct and unable to cope with situations demanding originality? As long as Pollux and Polly lived on Little River, they never again built an underwater lodge—nor attempted any large damming projects.

When the flood subsided, they retreated into a nearby ravine and dug a den in a small draw near the water line. There they decided to remain, since it was well concealed. And that would have solved their problem, except for a mistake of their own making.

As soon as possible, they dammed the small draw. Why they did this, only their Creator would know. It had no connection with their quest for food, which was becoming more plentiful with each lengthening day and budding plant.

It was this small dam that gave the beavers away. Ferret-eyes, free long since, was on the prowl. By chance, he saw the obstacle near the entrance to their draw, across the stream. He crossed Little River and explored the ravine from end to end. But he was looking for a beaver lodge and missed the concealed den opening in the small draw. The beavers were there—he could see their tracks—so he spent part of an afternoon watching, rifle in hand. Then he set traps.

First to be caught was a raccoon, exploring the dam for possible frogs. And when a man came and killed him, after hours of torment, both beavers knew the fear of death. Thus was reborn a mistrust of mankind, which had lain semidormant during their captivity, since they had noticed the traps before the raccoon was caught, and had smelled the familiar man-odor about them.

Later, when a rifle shot rang out and a bullet spattered on a rock within inches of Pollux' head, the fear grew. Mankind had become their enemy, now that their hideaway was discovered, and more than ever their instincts warned them to mistrust everything. Thereafter, they ventured outside their den only after owl dusk.

Then Pollux stepped into a trap that had been set cun-

ningly in a path he had made for Polly and himself. For
the rest of that night, he struggled in the grip of a merciless
thing that numbed his forepaw and made his leg bleed
where the bone had pierced through. Polly stood by, but
could do nothing against this enigma of misery.

In the morning, Ferret-eyes crossed Little River, entered
the ravine, and found Pollux. He picked up a rock and
flung it at the beaver's head, but so swiftly did Pollux
dodge that the missile struck only a glancing blow and
stunned him. The man had picked up another rock, when
a voice at the ravine entrance shouted "Hey!" He whirled
about, to face the lumberman, arriving revolver in hand.
"All right—get that beaver out of your trap."

"Ah cain't," whined the outlaw. "He'll bite me."

"Oh yeah? Get busy, or I'll blast your ears off. We've
been watching you for a week."

Pollux watched the men leave before he hobbled into his
den. For the rest of his life, he would be partly crippled,
and only the fact that he was sick and unable to travel
kept Polly and himself from abandoning their den at
once. By the time his leg had healed, it was too late, for
Polly was about to bear her litter.

During this period no more human beings bothered the
beavers, for the lumberman had issued strict orders, while
Ferret-eyes went to jail again and thereafter stayed away
from Little River.

Polly's five kits were born in mid-April—a blessed event
she had deferred while at the San Francisco Exposition.
Within a few weeks, the little ones began solid diet, and
by the end of summer, they were one third the size of their
parents. These youngsters would be three years in maturing,
after which they would mate with the offspring of the
other pair of beavers, who had settled upstream.

The next year brought another litter of kits, while the five
from the previous season continued to live at home. This,
the parents allowed, and would, until the youngsters be-

came two-year-olds when, by the laws of beaverdom, they were expected to go out into the world on their own.

It was during this second year's summer that trouble again came to Pollux and Polly. The lumber company decided to resume operation on a rail line that ran along Little River on the beavers' side. Up to now, the family had regarded the embankment, with its occasional trout fisherman, as part of their property.

Great, therefore, was their dismay when a section gang fell noisily to work and rattled back and forth on speeders. But this was as nothing later, when the first train roared by. Thereafter, traffic was continuous and ground-shaking. Also, their dam had been discovered several times by interested, if harmless, visitors.

The situation had become untenable, if not actually perilous. And so, when the younger litter was able to travel, Pollux and Polly decided to move. The older youngsters were able to fend for themselves now, and a couple of them decided to remain. The rest, piloted by their parents, started downstream one night.

Pollux knew where he wanted to go. There was a long, quiet stretch of water, heavily banked with trees and brush, that lay below the town, toward the sea. To get to it, they had to follow Little River as it flowed through the town. During the hush of the small hours, they passed through in safety and by daylight were established in the most secluded spot they had yet known. At once, the family set to work digging a den—a job Pollux found difficult to do without help because of his crippled forepaw.

For five years, Pollux and Polly lived and raised their young in the lower estuary of Little River, within sound of the sea. And they probably would have finished their life span of some fifteen years there, had it not been for their urge to build dams.

Little River could not be handled—that they knew—but a small stream flowing down from a nearby meadow was

ideal, as they saw it. Again and again they set up dams, only
to have them destroyed by a neighboring rancher because
they flooded his pasture lands.

The rancher was a kindly disposed man, but his patience
had limits. In the fifth spring, when his pasture was flooded
several times, he decided to take action. He set a large box
trap near the dam and baited it with carrots. The first night,
a two-year-old was caught, but he gnawed his way out,
unaware that he had been trapped. Next day, the rancher
lined the box with sheet metal.

After that, several youngsters were caught in quick succession. They were released in a group of fresh-water
tarns a couple of miles down the coast, and near other
streams. Then word got about among the colony that the
box was to be avoided, and catches ceased. The rancher
then took his trap away in hopes that the remaining beavers
would forget. This, he reasoned, they would do before long,
since no animals had been killed in it to leave an emanation
of death.

Pollux, as the years increased upon him, traveled less
and less, especially during cold weather, when his crippled
forepaw pained him. Construction and repair of the dams
were left increasingly to the newer generations, although
most of these showed a desire to migrate after a time. Now,
with several of his helpers missing, he decided to visit the
dam and inspect. Also, it happened that the rancher had
decided that day to set his trap again.

Pollux looked at the box with interest. The smell of
carrots reminded him of nighttime raids on the rancher's
garden. That it was the work of mankind did not concern
him as long as no human beings were in sight. Forgotten
was the fact that just such a contrivance had caught him
and his mate in their younger days. After inspecting the
dam, he went into the trap, picked up the carrots—and
was caught.

His first reaction was anger, which changed to fear when

he began to realize he could not free himself. Again and again he flung his bulk against the barrier where he had entered. But the box was well built, and morning found him still in it, rather the worse for shock, when the rancher and his hired man arrived.

The two men carried the trap with its prisoner back to the farmyard, where their families gathered about to peek at the big beaver. "I'd give a dime to know what that fellow weighs," said the hired man.

"That's easy," said the rancher. "Put the trap and contents on the scales. Then, later, weigh the empty box. Difference will be the beaver, won't it?"

"What a brain!" laughed the hired man. "Where'll we take him?"

The rancher's eyes were twinkling. "You know, Al," he said, "I'll bet this is one of the original batch our lumberman friend brought up from the exposition. This one is the boss beaver that engineered that pesky dam for sure. So—let's take him to Mr. Lumberman's hunting preserve on Widow White Creek and turn him loose. That's fair enough, eh?"

"Good deal!" agreed the hired man. "And there's a dam and big pond over there that ought to be just right for beavers."

"Let's go!" said the rancher.

And so Pollux found himself in a rushy, tree-lined pond on a stream of its own that flowed directly into the Pacific, some six miles south of his Little River abode. Back at the ranch, they found that the senior beaver weighed forty-six pounds.

Except for a hunting cabin, a quarter mile away, the new location was quite isolated, while it was wooded to the most exacting beaver's taste. But to all of this, Pollux was unresponsive. Polly was not there. Late that night, he left and started back.

Beyond analysis is the guiding force that took Pollux

down to the beach, and pointed his nose northward toward Little River mouth. Never had he actually seen the ocean before, although he had lived within sound of it for five years. To his eyes, it was a vast and active lake whose waters, he found, were too bitter to swim. Step by painful step, he limped along the sand toward his goal. Then dawn brought men to dig clams, and so he hid in a mass of driftwood less than two miles from his starting point.

Polly had become worried that morning, back at Little River, when Pollux did not return. Never had he stayed away for so long. By evening, she was frightened and set out to look for him. When she got to the trap, drawn by Pollux' scent, she stopped. Here was where he had been—there was no mistaking that. Into the box she went, pushed the carrots aside to smell further—and was caught.

"That's the big fellow's mate, I'll bet," the rancher said, next morning.

"Shall we take her to him?" asked the hired man.

"Right. Then I think our headache with the dams will be over. They were the pair that dreamed up that job."

Thus, a few hours after Pollux left, Polly was released in the lumberman's pond on Widow White Creek. That her mate had been there was obvious, and she set out at once to follow his trail. Although she was weighted with young, Polly traveled much the faster and would have caught up with him, had it not been for the clam diggers. One of them saw her following the edge of the seashore and fired a shot at her. Others joined the chase, and the female beaver was driven into the sea.

The pounding of the breakers did not concern her, but their saltiness had her strangling almost at once. For a time, she was able to keep breathing, but finally was forced ashore—to be shot at as soon as she emerged from the surf. Again she retreated into the sea, while an excited group of men ran along the beach. When Polly raised her head among the combers for air, sharp eyes spotted her, and bullets pinged off the water. Her strength was ebbing fast from paroxysms of coughing, and it was only a matter of minutes until a bullet would find its mark. Then a game warden, attracted by the shooting, arrived on the scene.

"It's an otter, or something," onlookers told him.

"Well, let it alone. You are breaking the law," the warden said, and the diggers went back to their clams.

But the warden was interested and, when he saw what looked like a half-drowned spaniel floundering in the surf downshore, he slipped away by himself to investigate. When he found the animal was a beaver, his surprise was complete. He carried her up to a mass of driftwood to avoid kill-hungry eyes. That a beaver should sicken to the point of drowning, even in the ocean, seemed incredible, although the animal was heavy with young. After a time, Polly retched and retreated under the driftwood, where the warden wisely decided to let her stay, while he went back to his patrol, a puzzled man.

For the rest of the day, both Pollux and Polly stayed in their driftwood hideouts, not two hundred yards apart. With rising tide the clam diggers left, and the beach turned quiet. When the wind slowed at nightfall, the beavers caught each other's scent and came out to investigate. Their reunion could have lacked fervor from a human standpoint, but it was all the more real because they were cut off and facing the unknown.

One tie they had, however. That was the route back to Widow White Creek pond. Ahead lay more of the unknown, since neither of them knew how far away Little River might be, nor what perils lay between. Behind was a known haven—and they were bewildered and tired. They turned back. . . .

In the dense alders and willows along Widow White Creek, a hundred yards upstream from the pond, Pollux and Polly found their promised land. The stream was too small for destructive floods, and so they built a dam across it and—once again—a permanent lodge for their declining days.

And that is how the beavers got their start in the lumberman's preserve—a matter which its astonished owner was at loss to explain. He was all the more amazed, one morning, when he caught a glimpse of Pollux repairing a barrier across a culvert which the lumberman wanted to keep open, but which Pollux was determined should stay closed.

"It's the beaver that lawbreaker fellow caught in the trap, for sure," he soliloquized. "Limps with the same leg. But how did he get here—swim the ocean? Fair enough, old-timer—may your tribe increase. . . ."

Saga of a Giant

Of all the waters in the Redwood Empire of California, Smith River seems closest to its Creator's primal theme. It flows today as it did when white men first saw it—cool and crystalline-beryl, unsullied, and unchecked. Snow-mantled mountains give it birth, rock-hewn gorges guide its path, and, toward the last, it dawdles down a valley of centuries-old redwood forests to wander away to sea.

And up that river come certain giant trout, home from the Pacific when the spawning call summons them to the life waters of their birth.

Mysterious are these Smith River giants, shy and slow to bite, but so incredibly strong that few have been taken, and then only by a blend of luck and skill. Experts have been baffled, costly tackle ruined—nor has the question of their origin been settled.

. . . What mankind might have thought meant nothing to Irideus the giant trout, two miles out at sea one April morning, when he cruised into a current tinged with Smith River's water. Although his species would not spawn until winter, some nameless concourse within his life spark responded to that water, for it emanated from the stream of his nativity. More than three years had passed since he had left it as an eight-inch youngster to go to sea. Now, an urge actuated his consciousness to return to the river and resume life in fresh water.

True, he had been back to Smith River briefly as a twenty-inch grilse, two winters before. But all he had wanted then was to eat the eggs of spawning salmon and enjoy the taste of running water again. Now, he was coming into maturity and would procreate during his fifth year of life.

Irideus, however, was not doomed to die after his mating saga, as would his remote relative, the Pacific salmon, since he was a true trout. As such, he was the more favored of Nature and might survive several spawning runs. Nor did he need to go away to sea, except through choice. Rather, his instinct had led him downstream into deep water because food was more abundant there. In an inland river, he would have sought a lake.

Slowly, easily, the great trout swung into the aerated current that had been Smith River. A north wind was blowing whitecaps on the surface, but the water beneath was calm, and it pleased his taste. He quickened his pace —a near three feet of streamlined strength, broad of tail and deep of flank, while his weight neared thirty pounds.

Three years of life in salt water had bleached Irideus to a salmon-silveryness, shrinking the spots on his body to buckshot size. A few weeks in fresh water, however, would darken his sheen and bring back the reddish coloration to his cheeks and sides, while his speckles would double in size and number. And now, for reasons no man could fathom, Irideus was going back to Smith River for an indefinite stay.

Ahead of him, Orca the killer whale was on the prowl for any prey that took his fancy, including seals. Irideus was not afraid of killer whales, but he did not like to be chased. He let himself sink until the visibility about him darkened to blue velvet, and continued ahead. A mile farther in, he rose to the surface to seek out the Smith River current again. A school of cutthroat trout, handsome fellows averaging a foot in length, showed ahead of him. These, too, had come from Smith River, but only to feed briefly in salt water and return to the stream. They looked appetizing.

Like a jet-missile, Irideus shot into their midst before they realized their danger—and the taste of fresh-water fish was good. He continued toward his destination with accelerated speed. He was a quarter mile off the surf by Smith River mouth when a herd of sea lions spotted him. As one animal, they raced toward the big fish, converging from several directions. Irideus was annoyed. He flashed upward and made a tarponlike leap as the water churned beneath him.

Then he raced off at top speed, concentrating every fiber of his explosive strength into the getaway. Seconds later he arrived at Smith River bar. Behind him, the baffled sea lions milled about, each certain that another of its herd mates had caught the coveted prey. A lone sea lion made a run at him inside the river's lagoon, but he evaded it as easily as a stag would bypass a lumbering bull.

Smith River is open to fishermen as far up as tidewater all year. Although the lagoon at its mouth is not large, several boats were trolling back and forth in it. Irideus had seen boats at sea, and felt wary of them. Accordingly, he swung near shore and passed under an anchored float. There he noticed a chunk of salmon roe, with an odor-haze rising from it. Vistas of his grilse days, when he had raided salmon redds in the river, came back. He picked up the roe with one scoop of his massive jaw.

On the float, a woman jerked her casting rod when she felt the strike—and the panic was on! Her screams startled seagulls overhead, while her husband rushed to the rescue. But all he could do was to hang on, stunned and stuttering, while the reel emptied itself of line in one rush.

The woman was more vocal. "That was my fish and you lost it!" she shrilled.

"Fish, hell!" growled the man. "You snagged a sea lion."

Irideus was towing ninety yards of fish line, but he was

not concerned, now that it no longer resisted. Nor did the hook in his jaw trouble him especially, while the salmon roe had been enjoyable. He veered across the lagoon and headed upstream, swimming leisurely near the surface. Behind him, the line curved in a long bight just as a small boat with an outboard motor crossed over it. A sudden tug brought him about when the line end caught in the boat's propeller.

This time, Irideus was angry. Something was affronting his dignity. He blasted ahead like a berserk bull. The line held just long enough to twitch the boat—and then he was free, with only the hook in his mouth. But this experience had been painful. He broke water with a great slash, while the boat's occupants yelled.

That encounter with the boat loosened the hook in Irideus' jaw. What had been a perforation was now a slit. He shook his head in anger, and the hook slipped free to sink into the ooze below, forever removed from mankind's will to harm. In moments, he had forgotten the matter and was cruising upstream again.

Smith River was still high from an eighty-inch rainy season and heavy snows in the mountains. However, because of the rocky uplands in which it originated, the water already was emerald-clear. Irideus did not like so much sunlight penetrating into his element. And so, when he reached a deep pool, a mile or more upstream, he sought shelter for the rest of the day. He was in no hurry.

The water had darkened with afternoon's wane, and Irideus was becoming restive, when a clump of wriggling worms drifted by. He twitched his fins involuntarily, for these aroused formless memories of his fingerling days, when a worm was a prized delicacy. But these did not seem worthy of pursuit, and he settled back. None the less, their blood aroma had stirred something in his being. When another and larger bunch of worms came along, he drifted

toward them with a stroke of his powerful tail and engulfed
them as easily as he would breathe.

He turned back—and became aware of a resistance as
something stung the roof of his mouth. He shook his head
to rid himself of this annoyance—and the resistance
changed to a positive pull. This reminded him of the morning's skirmish with the boat. He swung clear of his shelter
and drove upstream.

The man who had been fishing atop a log jam had sense
enough to clamp down at the last and break the leader before he lost all his line. He reeled in the slack wide-eyed.
"Felt like I'd hooked a locomotive," he said. "Probably a
big sturgeon."

"I dunno," hazarded another. "There's some funny fish
in this river, and they ain't sturgeons."

Now that he was started, Irideus stayed under way.
Within a mile, he was clear of the last reach of tidewater
and had left the fishermen behind. Nor would he be bothered again until the season opened upstream, late in May.
Through riffles and pools he ascended, feeding upon an
occasional crawfish. He was aware of the hook in his mouth,
but would rid himself of it in due course. As night came
on, he continued upstream with an easy, tireless pace.

Smith River was not swift as yet, since Irideus was still
in the lower confines of its timbered valley. Massive redwood trees—as symbolic of their kind as the big trout was
of his own—towered against a moonlit sky and whispered
reminiscences of the ages to the night breeze. Emblematic
of life's tenacity were these sequoia sempervirens, for
among them were patriarchs that had known earth in the
days of ancient Rome and were into their middle age before Columbus was born. To these, the advent of the oldest
settler into Smith River valley was as last season's June bug.

It cannot be said that Irideus was aware of the templed
aisles and hills about him, since his was a world apart. But
their essence was in the water, and that stimulated him. No

longer did he belong to the sea. This was what he wanted
and, toward morning, he felt the increasing challenge of
Smith River as its water quickened with every mile upstream.

Accordingly, he was in a mood to rest when he charged
up a long riffle and entered a pool deep in a gorge, where
the south fork of Smith River meets the main stream. This
is a stretch of water over a quarter mile in length, and as
much as forty feet deep in places. A few of his kind already
were there, brought in by the same urge, and food was
abundant. He slowed to a stop like a liner coming to dock.
Here he would stay for a time, ten miles in from the sea.

In the days that followed, more giant trout arrived at the
confluence pool. Some schooled together and left for the
upper reaches of the south fork where, instinct told them,
other pools awaited their advent. Others proceeded up the
main river to seek rendezvous. But Irideus, who was larger
than the rest, chose to stay in the confluence pool. He was
in no hurry.

Steelhead trout were passing through, both up and downstream, but the giants ignored these smaller rainbow relatives and stayed by themselves. The largest steelhead might
have weighed fifteen pounds—scarcely the weight of the
smallest giant.

Then fishing season opened. The quiet of the confluence
pool was disturbed by small boats sputtering about, while
men cast from the rocks at the base of the cliffs. Steelhead
and cutthroat trout were being taken, but the giants
wanted nothing of mankind's lures. Up and down the
length of the pool they moved, keeping as far from the
boats as possible. And whenever a spinner was cast from
above, they scattered from the vicinity of its splash. That
night, several of his kind left for points upstream. But
Irideus stayed on.

One morning at dawn, a master fisherman came down
the cliff to the pool. He preferred to fish by himself, even

as Irideus chose to travel alone. He noted with satisfaction that an upcanyon breeze was rippling the water just enough for fly fishing. Silently as an otter, the man glided among the rocks to his chosen place. Then he cast out a large, red-bodied fly with white streamer wings. So expertly did he work that it fluttered and fell to the surface like a spent bug.

Irideus might have been ten feet beneath when the fly landed. He rose like a goldfish when food is strewn upon its tank surface, and gulped the fly with an audible pop. Suddenly the fly seemed to want to get away. It jerked and stung. At that precise instant, Irideus decided this was not what he wanted and tried to spit it out. But a finished angler had set the hook. It was too late.

Irideus did not fly into a leaping panic as would his lesser kin, the steelhead-rainbows. Rather, he was irked. He shook his head several times to rid himself of this nuisance and then decided to leave the immediate vicinity.

For some fifty yards, he proceeded at an even pace, conscious of the pull at the corner of his jaw. Then the strain increased. Irideus sped up, as if to offset it. The pull increased still more. A cyclonic rage swept through the giant trout. Like a high-powered automobile whose throttle is suddenly opened, he blasted ahead, raising a bulge on the surface behind him.

But the water at the upper end of the pool was becoming too shallow—perhaps five feet. Irideus did not like this. He put about and started back for the deepest area, some two hundred yards downstream. As he did, the pull slackened. On the way, he passed his adversary, on a rock, stripping in line with perspiring haste.

Irideus had gone perhaps ten yards past the rock when the pull took hold again. He accelerated at once, and burst three feet into the air, his sides reflecting reddish in the early morning light. His great speckled tail struck the water with a whack, like a board, and he disappeared in a welter of foam and waves.

The man held back on his line as much as he dared, and breathed a prayer. In a lifetime of trout fishing, he never had hooked one like this. Perspiration ran off his eyebrows and onto his glasses.

Irideus was puzzled and outraged. When he reached the far side of deep water, he put about again—and again the pull slackened. He forged ahead and down until he was on the bottom, forty feet below. There he sulked, while the fly kept pulling. Several times it twanged as the fisherman struck the butt of his rod with a rock.

A basic anger was coming over Irideus, and now he knew that he was going to leave the confluence pool. He started upstream again, his powerful tail swinging as evenly as the strokes of a pendulum. And just as evenly, the fly in his jaw tried to slow him down. But Irideus already had half forgotten the fly as he proceeded up the middle of the pool. He was on his way.

Back on the rock, a despairing man watched his line melt down with the squall of his reel, nor could he do anything about it. He might as well have had hold of a submarine. At the last, when his two hundred and thirty yards of line had shrunk down to a few feet, he increased resistance to the breaking point. But the steady pull neither sped up nor decreased. At the end, he clamped down. Out at Irideus' end of the line, the leader snapped.

Irideus scarcely noticed when the fly ceased to resist. He was dominated by one idea, nor would he stop until oncoming sunlight put him to shelter in some deep hole upstream. When he got around to it, he would rid himself of the fly by rubbing his jaws against rocks and tree roots until it was dislodged. He was in no hurry. . . .

Two days later, Irideus ran afoul of another danger. Morning had brought him to rest in a pool, miles upstream, but he was still in a mood to feed, despite several tasty crawfish that had come his way. A school of small trout darted by, and he raced up a riffle after them, churning the shallow water into foam.

Purpose accomplished, he turned back—and ran into something that closed about him like a tangle of seaweed. He spurted ahead to get away from this impediment but drove deeper into it instead—and was enveloped in a seine net. Shouting men plunged into the riffle. In vain he thrashed in an effort to escape. The tangle only increased. He was caught.

The men's purpose was legitimate enough. They were state fish and game researchers who wanted specimens of the Smith River giants for study. Now they had one of the best. Irideus was pulled ashore in an unceremonious hurry.

"Just what the doctor ordered," said the project leader. "Let's put him in the live-box and take him back to head-quarters."

For the first time in an otherwise capably conducted existence, Irideus underwent an abandonment of terror and confusion. Nothing in his background had prepared him for this, and so his instincts could offer no guidance. He twisted and writhed with desperate strength, but the meshes of the net held him fast.

Carefully the men untangled him and, with rubber-gloved hands, placed him in a large wooden box submerged in the mouth of a small creek. Holes in each end of this box, together with a perforated lid, gave ample water circulation.

Irideus sank to the bottom of the live-box, his tail barely moving. Only his laboring gill cheeks gave evidence of the stress he had undergone. Men peeked through at him from above and shook their heads in admiration. Then one of them thumped the side of the box with a rock. Instantly Irideus exploded. For minutes on end he smashed back and forth, battering his nose against the ends of the box until blood began to show. His madly thrashing tail kicked foam through the perforated lid like geyser eruptions—while the culprit who had touched him off received an all-around cursing.

Then the men placed a canvas atop the box. In the comparative darkness, Irideus subsided. But every nerve fiber in his body was aquiver, for instinct cried out that he was a captive and that his life was forfeit—even as prey he had caught all his life.

Later in the day Irideus was subjected to further indignities. Rubber-gloved hands reached down into the live-box, cornered him after another struggle, wrapped him in a dripping wet burlap, and rushed him to a nearby truck.

Here he was plopped into a metal tank full of chilled water, aerated by a motor-driven pump. A lid was hastily clamped down, but, in the total darkness, Irideus remained quiet.

A few minutes later, however, when the entire tank began to rumble and vibrate from the truck getting under way, he went berserk. No excited steelhead-rainbow, wracked with fear and tension, could have approached him for violence of effort. Nor did he cease until he floated on his side, exhausted and beaten. Thus the men found him when the truck arrived at their trout hatchery-headquarters an hour later. Gently they lifted the gasping giant out and placed him in a large weir, spring-fed and covered by a high, arched screen.

During the night, Irideus recovered his strength, and morning found him in the darkest corner of the weir, awaiting he knew not what. During the predaylight hours, he had searched this strange pool for a way out, since instinct warned him that he was still in jeopardy. But when a man looked at him from above, he did not move. Food, in the form of fresh horse meat, he ignored.

Irideus' weir-prison was large enough that he felt no inclination to batter against its walls. Time and again, however, he tried to leap out—only to encounter the screen and fall back. This barrier was placed high enough above the water that he could not hit it with much force. Even so, as the days went by, he began to take on a somewhat ragged appearance.

Then he was subjected to still further indignities. Men with gaping nets chased him to and fro until he was caught and brought to the surface. There, while thrashing and squirming, he was examined by biologists and interested students.

What may have transpired in the giant trout's consciousness, as the weeks went by, must remain unknown. Suffice it to say that, in time, he seemed to tame down. When the nets began their chase, he would allow himself to be caught with token resistance. Also, he had long since resumed feeding and especially relished tidbits like worms and salmon roe. But he was no longer the prime specimen he had been when the men took him from Smith River.

Fall came to the Redwood Empire, and with it the spawning urge to the trout and salmon tribes. It was in their blood, in the water, and in the very air above the water. In the confines of his weir, Irideus felt it as surely as if he had been somewhere up in the headwaters of Smith River. Every molecule of his being cried out to get away and start upstream. Again and again he leaped with all his strength into the air, hitting the overhead screen with such force that he left scales clinging to it.

The hatchery manager was vexed, since no instructions had come to release the splendid captive or to do anything more about the matter. His colleagues' interest, apparently, had shifted to other topics. Toward Irideus he felt only sympathy, and hoped the giant trout would not injure himself and become diseased.

Then one night someone tried to cut the wire covering the weir and was driven off by the hatchery's dog—and therefrom the manager got an idea. Next night there was a longer slash in the wire, and Irideus was missing. On the books he was entered as stolen . . . with evidence to show, should anyone be interested.

To Irideus, all of this meant nothing. He was caught in the usual manner, then dumped into a tank truck for a short journey. He had become so accustomed to the vagaries of mankind by now, however, that he did almost no thrashing en route. Then he was netted out of the tank and dumped into a body of water that fairly teemed with the spawning call. One swirl of his spade-shaped tail, and he was away into its cool depths.

"Why didn't you put him in the ocean, dad?" the manager's son asked when it was over. "Then he could have gone back to the Smith River. He won't like it here, will he?"

"Good question," his father replied. "To put him in salt water would have been too sudden a change. Here in Sequoia Creek lagoon, he will have to stay in fresh water until the stream rises later in the season and breaks her open into the sea. Then he can get out whenever he wants. Meanwhile, he'll feed on everything in sight."

True to the manager's prediction, Irideus began almost at once to feed. He gorged on small trout, sticklebacks, minnows, crawdads, young eels, and even crunched up quantities of water snails. Several times he leaped at birds that sidled down bended willow branches to drink. Within ten days, he was his vibrant self again.

But with increasing strength, Irideus became ever more restless and irritated. Something was wrong here. He could not go upstream because the water was too low. Nor could he get away to sea, since the creek's lagoon mouth was sanded shut until the rains came. Out of sheer bad temper he began chasing anything he saw, even to trout too large to swallow. And this got him into trouble.

An occasional boat was trolling Sequoia Creek lagoon, for the cutthroat trout were biting, and they were prime. One overcast afternoon, a boat went churning over Irideus' lair beneath a tangle of redwood stumps. Soon thereafter, a silvery wobbler zigzagged by. Quivering with rage, Irideus shot out and clamped onto it with such force that the boat was jarred and the fisherman's reel shrieked.

This fisherman, however, was no sportsman. He was after meat, and had heavy salmon tackle with plenty of line. He gripped his pole and horsed back, while the pull of the big fish swung the boat off course.

A siwash hook had gone through Irideus' nose. This pained and enraged him. He cut across the lagoon with unbelievable speed and leaped high into the air. The man cried out involuntarily and broke into a sweat.

This time, Irideus was not calmly unconcerned, as he had been when hooked before. Perhaps some instinct—perhaps the messenger of Manitou, who watches over all wild things—warned him that now he was in deadly peril . . . that if he failed, this was the end.

Had the giant trout been hooked through the lower jaw, he would have been unable to breathe freely, since all fishes must open and close that appendage to force oxygen-giving water through their gills. Thus the hook in Irideus' nose, while painful, did not interfere with his breathing. And so his strength was available in full—even if it only prolonged the end.

Sequoia Creek lagoon has a number of densely thicketed inlets and sloughs. Irideus at once drove toward one of these, seeking a place to get away from this menace that pulled more strongly than anything he had experienced. But his adversary was wise in the ways of fish. He tightened down on his heavy reel and horsed the pole by main strength until his prey turned back toward open water. The strain on the man's tackle was great—but it held together.

Some inner prompting then led Irideus across Sequoia Creek lagoon and, despite the man's efforts to stop him, the great trout reached deep water near where the creek's mouth would open when rising floods burst the lagoon into the sea. Here he sulked on the bottom, lashing his head, until the strain became all but unbearable.

Inch by grudging inch he gave ground. Slowly, but with awful sureness, he was being pulled up from deep water, while the strength of his resistance held the boat stationary. Then the man sped up his motor, and Irideus was dragged into shallower water. The man beached his boat and sprang ashore, straining against his quarry.

Irideus' vitality was ebbing. He was winnowing back and forth in less than four feet of water by now, and the radius of each swing was less than the last. Foot by foot, the reel was pumping him in. The will to battle was leaving him now, and he pulled back sullenly but without fervor. Once or twice he rolled off balance, recovered with a sweep of his still powerful tail, but was unable to hold his own. It had been some time since the reel squalled under duress. Turn by turn, the line was coming in. Turn by turn, Irideus was being dragged ashore—and to the end.

What goes on in the consciousness of a beaten thing as it feels the approach of doom? Perhaps a merciful angel lulls the awareness of defeat, and the primal instinct drowses. Men who have survived such experiences find it difficult to describe them afterward.

. . . Now siwash hooks have an unusually long barb, which makes them penetrate deeply. But the very length of these barbs can be their weakness. Irideous' consciousness was still alert enough to feel that the man plunging into the water toward him was an enemy. A renewed burst of strength—a thoroughbred's reserve—upwelled through him. He half leaped out of water and charged away with a resurgence of vitality that caught the man off guard. He dropped his gaff hook and clamped down on his reel. Heavy cuttyhunk line stretched with strain—and the overworked siwash hook's barb snapped off clean.

Irideus swam weakly down the lagoon until he reached deep water again, where he rested. Ashore, the man examined his broken hook and cursed all tackle, fish, and the world in general.

Rain came to the Redwood Empire's timbered sweep, and Sequoia Creek rose and turned opaque. There was a summons in that rise. Also, the creek was high enough now that Irideus could go upstream. But he hesitated. This was not his home water, and none of his kind were in it.

Inch by inch, Sequoia Creek lagoon rose. Heavy surf pounded the sand bar that separated it from the sea. On the third day of rain, a trickle spilled over from the lagoon and met salt water. An hour later, Sequoia Creek was flowing thirty feet wide into the sea.

Irideus was aware of the sudden outflow that sucked much of the lagoon's water into the sea. Then a high tide crested in through the newly created opening, and the lagoon's water turned brackish. A school of salmon came in, and fishermen appeared in quantity. Irideus liked none of this and retreated to his lair.

The presence of salt water was increasingly upon the giant trout as its pungence permeated the redwood stump tangle where he held forth. When the tide receded, widening the lagoon mouth to fifty feet, he circled into it but turned back.

An incoming tide, as night came on, brought in a few smelt. One of these swam by Irideus' lair. He shot out and swallowed it with one gulp—and the taste of salt-water fish was good.

When the tide reached its peak, he drifted through the lagoon mouth and into the surf as if that had been his regular routine all along. In moments he was through the breakers and into deep water. Smith River mouth was over fifty miles to the north. Irideus turned toward it, actuated by a homing call as ageless as the ancestry that had begot him. Others of the giant trout tribe would be coming in now. Perhaps the mate of his choice was among them. Irideus would find her by unerring selection. Together they would go upstream to the spawning riffles where their lives had begun . . . there to procreate as their Creator intended. . . .

This time, Irideus was in a hurry.

The Refuge

An aura of peace and quiet hovered over the secluded pond among the redwoods of Freshwater Valley. Last rays of the setting sun caressed timber-clad hills in a benediction of shadow and gold. Not so much as a catspaw riffled the water's calm. Bullfrogs chorused a muted overture from reed beds along the shore, while a brood of wild ducks twittered response. In a secret bower, an elfin owl fluted its hidden-spring note. It was that pause in retrospect at the edge of nightfall, when forest, hills, and water commune at vesper.

A light splash sounded from a grass-grown islet in the pond's middle. Waves rippled in a three-quarter circle as a doe left her retreat and started swimming toward shore.

Life had not always been so benign for the young mother deer as it appeared this evening. Bobcats and an occasional cougar from the hills had threatened her fawnhood and early maturity. But it was not until a pack of dogs chased her into the water at Freshwater Pond that she had become aware of the islet and learned that it seemed to offer a refuge from four-footed foes ashore.

Thereafter, she slept on the islet and no longer wandered far from Freshwater Pond when at feed. Now her first fawn lay bedded in the islet's grass, sheltered by a small clump of willows—secure from big cats and, apparently, dogs.

The newborn fawn was a spotted sprite, no larger than a hare. True to the dictate of deerdom, he lay motionless in his nest until his mother should return. Not so much as the twitch of an ear gave clue to his presence, for experience had impressed it into the subconsciousness of his race that the safety and survival of its young depended upon complete quiet when left alone.

Freshwater Pond covered an area of some twenty acres. Long ago, it had been used for log storage when a lumber company felled many of the age-old redwood trees in Freshwater Valley. Now, in timeless harmony, Nature had reclaimed her own after mankind's enterprises had moved away, and it was part of an estate owned and protected by a benevolent doctor who lived in a wooded glen, a mile away.

The sprite was too recently arrived into life to be aware of anything except food and the compulsion to remain quiet while his mother was away. His liquid-dark eyes were closed, and so he did not see a shadow that drifted over his nest as silently as thought.

Hush-wing, the great horned owl, might have been an enemy, for his tribe is known to relish young fawn. But Hush-wing, although he had observed Sprite, was more interested in a colony of water rats at the islet's edge. He swooped suddenly. Broad wings beat against the grass, followed by an agonized squeal, and the big bird rose, prey in talons, and banked toward shore.

Sprite felt a chill riffle down his spine but, outside of an involuntary shrinking, he made no move, nor did he open his eyes. But palpitating instinct was warning him that he had come into a world in which he, like the water rats, was one of the hunted. So it had always been with his kind.

He was still curled into a tight little bundle when a splash at the water's edge announced his mother's return. In moments, his soft nose was muzzling against her side in search of that food which no young mammal has to be told is its heritage. Warmth from the life-giving milk coursed through his body, and he relaxed. After nursing he fell asleep, while the rays of a gibbous moon filtered into the bower and spread lambence over the doe and her fawn.

For a time, Sprite's mother licked him fondly with her tongue, and then settled down to chewing a cud. Out in the pond, a trout splashed, while overhead a corps of nighthawks cried their sharp-noted "beerk" as they darted back and forth after insects.

When Sprite awakened an hour later, he found himself alone once more. But realization came so quickly that he only closed his eyes with elaborate slowness and did not alter his breathing.

A quiet splash—fast becoming familiar now—sounded at water's edge, followed by a parting of the grass. Sprite opened his eyes and raised his head in welcome—to encounter a sight that froze him. Instead of his mother's gentle touch and fragrant breath, he looked into a vixenlike face with a black band across glowing eyes. An odor emanated from it that was terrifying—the smell of a flesh eater, an enemy. Every particle of his being shrank from it in horror, but there was nothing he could do.

Moakwah the raccoon long ago had annexed the islet to his frog-and-crawfish hunting beat. When the doe moved out to it, neither animal paid the other the slightest heed. Their worlds had been so far apart that no trespassing was involved. But here was something that aroused Moakwah's curiosity and might even tempt his appetite. At all events, it called for investigation.

Moakwah sniffed for a few moments, and glanced over his shoulder by way of a checkup. Then he approached the furry, spotted bundle that smelled of young and tender meat. The raccoon had fed well that evening, and so he felt more inclined to play than kill, for his race is not given to useless slaughter. Besides, he never had seen so young a fawn before. He pushed the quivering mite with an exploratory paw, but still his find offered no resistance, nor did it attempt to flee.

Moakwah was becoming provoked. Perhaps he felt that his repute was being slighted, since other creatures that smelled like prey ran from him. He gave the fawn a nip on its hindquarters—and got a hint of succulent meat. His eyes glowed and he chirred roughly. Again he nipped— more sharply this time—and got a taste of blood.

That did it. He sprang atop his victim, seized it by the neck, and dragged it to the water's edge—since all things a raccoon eats must be washed first, if possible. But in his eagerness for a kill, Moakwah forgot that he was exposing himself. An angry bleat sounded from shore, followed instantly by a splash—and the mother deer was on the way. Moakwah knew what that meant, and he wanted no part of it. He let go of the fawn and plunged into the water toward the far shore.

The doe veered after the raccoon, swimming as she never had done before. Stroke by stroke she overtook him until, just before the two animals reached land, she struck him a slashing blow with her sharp forehoof. The intruder sank in a welter of bubbles and blood, but the fawn's mother did not stay to investigate. Back toward the islet she turned, with heart pounding and breath whistling.

Moakwah crawled ashore dazed and gashed, and sought refuge in a thicket. Thereafter, he deleted the islet from his beat.

Sprite lay where he had been dropped. Blood was trickling from his neck, and his breathing seemed to have ceased. High in a fire-seared redwood, Hush-wing watched with interest as the doe scrambled onto the islet and began anxiously inspecting her fawn.

For an hour, his mother licked and nudged Sprite by turns, and vainly tried to get him to nurse. The taste of his blood made her eyes glow with rage at first, but presently the bleeding ceased, and she was able to get him to stagger to his feet. Step by faltering step, she made way for him through the grass until the nest was reached. And there Sprite collapsed. After a time, he was able to seek nourishment, and finally relaxed into sleep. Thereafter, the doe watched the islet as never before.

The mother's first intimation that the islet was not a refuge from still other enemies came one night when a large dog, on the prowl from a ranch up the valley, jumped her near the pond. She did not try to lead him away, but ran confidently into the water and started for the islet. At once, the dog plunged in after her and, what was worse, began overtaking her.

For a confused moment, the doe continued toward the islet with increased speed. Then strategy came to the rescue, and she swung at right angles and headed for a tule bank. But the enemy was gaining rapidly and, before shallow water was reached, he was nipping at her hindquarters.

Then the deer did a strange thing. She plunged her head and chest partly under water and struck backwards with her hind feet. Twice she did this during the pursuit but missed. The third time, she caught the dog squarely on the chin.

When she emerged onto the tule bank and looked back, the foe was not in sight. A day or two later, his bloated body rose to the surface, where the prevailing wind drove it to the lee shore to disintegrate beneath the overhanging willows.

The air-conditioned summer of the Redwood Empire was past its peak and Sprite had grown into a sizeable youngster, when he began to indicate that he not only wanted to follow his mother to shore but that the islet did not furnish enough solid diet to satisfy his wants. The spots of his babyhood had begun to disappear, and he was turning that mellow chestnut with tan and whitish underparts which identifies the California coastal deer. But on his neck, partly covering the scars left by Moakwah, a snow-white streak was beginning to show, like a dash of paint.

An uneventful summer, except for an occasional human being along the shore, had partly quieted the doe's fears.

And, since she knew that Sprite's weaning time was not far away, she encouraged him to go for short swims about the islet. When her aggressive fawn plunged in after her one evening and kept determinedly at her side, she slowed down to keep from tiring him and proceeded toward shore. And so Sprite set foot onto the outside world for the first time.

This was the great adventure. Never before had he had space enough to break into a trot, since the islet was less than thirty feet in length and heavily overgrown. Here were spacious aisles under towering trees, where all manner of herbs, sprouts, and greens invited him to nibble. He watched his mother at feed and tried to sample everything she ate. From this hour on, milk would become an ever lesser part of his diet until he would no longer seek it at all. Later in the evening, his mother led him to a bed of water lilies at the pond's edge—a prized delicacy.

It was a thoroughly tired and drowsy Sprite whose mother had to push him into the water toward morning, before he would swim back to the islet. In fact, had it not been for her insistence, he would have bedded down in any one of a number of tempting dells ashore. As it was, he had napped briefly during the night. But the doe knew all too well the perils that lurked amid these exotic surroundings and would not relax until she and Sprite were safely back on their islet. No other place would suffice, since this unusual retreat offered the best security she would ever know.

Two months passed, and Sprite was entirely weaned. And with this came an increasing desire to forage farther from Freshwater Pond. But his mother was adamant. Safety lay within its shores, and she rarely ranged farther than a quarter mile from the water's edge.

One night in early fall, a strange thing happened. The doe and her now fair-sized fawn were visited by another deer. This one was a large fellow with a spread of antlers that looked menacing to Sprite, who, up to now, never had known there were other deer on earth except his mother. She, however, seemed excited by this visitor but not afraid. The two of them sniffed noses and, for a time, seemed to forget Sprite's existence.

Later, the big buck, who was Sprite's sire, left. But Sprite felt disturbed and resentful at this intrusion, and increasingly wanted to explore farther. Not that he was capable of thinking this out in any conscious manner—rather, the budding growth of what was to be a definite individuality was asserting itself.

A few nights later, two other does, with three fawns of Sprite's age, came down from the hills with the big buck accompanying them. Sprite was at first surprised, and then pleased, to meet others of his generation. After some butting of heads and gamboling about, he assumed leadership of the youngsters, while their mothers began to band together under the watchful eye of the big buck, since rutting season was near.

More than ever, Sprite felt an urge to lead the way into that world which beckoned from every direction, and from which his newly found companions had come. But the other fawns seemed to have a stronger herd instinct than himself—due perhaps to a more hazardous background— and stayed close to their parents.

Nor was Sprite allowed to stray far, although he tried more persistently each night. And each day at dawn he and his mother left the little band and swam out to their islet— there to stay until sundown—a procedure which Sprite liked less and less.

Then, one evening, Sprite got his chance. Another buck had come to the area, and there was to be a fight for mastery of the big buck's harem. Excitement was in the air, and discipline had sunk to a low ebb. That the bucks were to do battle meant nothing to Sprite. And so, when he and the most adventurous one of the other three fawns

found themselves out of their parents' sight, he struck out
for the nearby hills at once, with the other neophyte following.

By this time, the bucks were into combat. Had Sprite
and his companion but understood, this was an omen of
peril for them, since the sounds of struggle would attract
enemies from the deep timber.

It happened too quickly for comprehension. One moment, the two adventurers paused to nibble at a clump of
sprouts. An instant later, a spotted terror with yellow
eyes landed atop the other fawn. One thin cry, and its life
spark was snuffed out by a bobcat.

Sprite fled the scene of the killing on legs that had
changed to fear-charged springs. As he neared the pond,
Hush-wing swooped at him and then sheered away, apparently enjoying his joke. Sprite dodged and sailed over
a low fence, beside himself with dread.

For the rest of the night, he stayed close to the others,
while his dead companion's mother hunted for a time and
then returned to her surviving twin. Perhaps it was his first
experience with death that did it; perhaps his mother's
feeling of security toward the islet now reached him; but
that morning Sprite returned willingly to their hideout and
sought cover in the grass.

Rutting season passed, and the big buck went his way,
even as his defeated rival of a fortnight before. Falling
leaves carpeted the ground with russet and ochre pastels,
and there was a tang of frost in the clean fall air. Migrating
waterfowl were visiting the pond in Freshwater Valley in
noisy droves now, for in their own occult manner, they, too,
had learned that this place was a refuge, a sanctuary safe
from hunters. A golden haze brooded over hills and forest
in this, the Redwood Empire's most benign and beautiful
time of the year.

But alas for the good doctor's vigilance. Daytime hunters
knew better than to trespass Freshwater Pond, but jack-

lighters by night felt differently. The three does, with their
fawns, had approached a water-lily bed one evening and
started to feed, when a blinding glare suddenly enveloped
them. They stared into it, transfixed . . . and a salvo of
shots crashed from a willow copse.

Something seared Sprite's flank with a pain unlike anything he had known. He plunged blindly into the water,
where instinct led him toward the islet. On shore, the
marauders hastily gathered up their kill and fled toward
the road.

For three days Sprite lay in hiding in the nest of his
babyhood, a sick and wounded young thing, unable to
understand why his mother did not return. Fever wracked
him, followed by weakness from lack of food. He recoiled
in terror from every sound, even to the splash of a trout,
or Hush-wing's familiar hoot, while the distant yammering
of a dog made him tremble beyond control. He licked his
wound from time to time, and the taste of it added to his
misery. But his life entity was too strong to let go, and
during the third day the crisis passed and he relaxed into a
sound sleep.

That night, hunger drove him ashore, but he went with
the fear of a thing that knows its life is forfeit. Potential
menace lurked in every sight and sound, and he stayed
close to the pond. Instinct told him that death, in some
manner, had claimed his mother—even as the bobcat had
taken his companion, a few weeks before.

A few nights later, when his wound was well into healing,
Sprite got a great scare. Some creature was approaching
him through the brush. He dashed into the water, but a
falsetto protest made him look back. There, standing on
the shore, the picture of forlorn abandonment, was the
twin of the fawn that had been killed by the bobcat. A
trim, pixylike young female, she was the only other survivor
of the murdered little band. For a moment Sprite wavered.
Then he put back.

The two young deer touched noses, and something of the tragedy that had been their common lot was alleviated. No longer did they feel so terrified and lost. Thereafter they fed together—but at dawn, Sprite swam out to his islet, while Pixy stayed ashore.

Winter brought freezing winds and heavy rains. Snow fell low on the surrounding hills, and forage was none too abundant even in the protected valley. The two young deer were forced to widen their range, but always Sprite stayed within fair radius of the pond. And because he did, Pixy now stayed also—although she refused to swim out to the islet, despite Sprite's urging. Nor did he have authority to compel her, as once his mother had had with him.

Deeper and deeper lay the snows on the hills as January began its wane . . . and down from the hills came enemies, forced likewise to widen their range. Sprite and Pixy were well up into the doctor's pasture land one night, browsing at the foot of a timbered hill—when a fearsome thing sprang out of the woods and raced toward them in long, sinuous leaps. Here was a foe bigger by far than the bobcat that had killed Pixy's twin, tawny-colored somewhat like themselves, but with the glaring yellow eyes of a killer.

Straight for the pond on flying feet dashed the two young deer, with death gaining behind. Whatever communication may have passed between them is beyond human recording —but as one animal they hit the water and started for the islet. True, Pixy never had swum before, but that ability which is born into all four-footed creatures carried her through. Side by side, they swam toward safety, while a thwarted cougar paced the shore and snarled. Up in his redwood watchtower, Hush-wing watched with interest— and perhaps approval.

To Earth Reborn

Other than what his instincts might have told him, Chee-ho, the ring-necked pheasant knew nothing of the perils that awaited him in a free world—for Chee-ho had been one of a brood raised at a college in northwestern California, under the supervision of a game management professor and his class.

It had been a successful project, with ten of the dozen quail-like chicks growing into birds almost as large as their foster mother, a devoted Plymouth Rock hen. Now, however, the pheasants were a year old, and the professor had decided to leg-band them and liberate them in what seemed a perfect environment—the lower Mad River valley in the college's own Redwood Empire, where snow rarely fell and searing heat was unknown.

And so, Chee-ho and his kin-flock found themselves at liberty in a grassy field one bright spring morning. Redwood trees towered near by, while Mad River belied its name by riffling gently from pool to pool on its final lap to the Pacific Ocean.

That the surrounding forests and hills contained enemies was well known, but it was felt that these would not be too great a drawback in this bountiful countryside. Here were bottom lands teeming with food, while a timbered back country completed the picture. The professor and his class were delighted.

At first, Chee-ho craned his neck in bewilderment as his human friends disappeared, for never had he seen so much space. Then a grasshopper zipped by and alighted a few yards away. He ran after it and enjoyed his first tidbit of freedom. The others followed him, since they had no desire to separate. And since Chee-ho was the largest, they looked to him for leadership.

Chee-ho looked like a jewel—an exotic from another world—as the sunlight glinted on his burnished gold-and-reddish feathers by way of contrast with the somber background of the redwoods. Protuberant ear-tufts and red discs around his eyes gave his head a painted-owl appearance. His neck was black, with an offsetting ring of white at its base—as if generations of semidomesticity in his ancestral Orient had left their symbol. His buff-colored tail, barred with black, was longer than his body, while his short, broad wings were able to carry him a considerable distance —an asset thus far unused.

Two men were approaching the bouquet of pheasants. The birds did not feel alarmed, since men always had meant protection and food. Just now they felt uncertain, and the presence of human beings was reassuring. Several of the flock turned toward them with clucks of recognition. But something deep in Chee-ho's consciousness was on guard. Some awakening vibration was cautioning him. He paused with a chuck-chuck that was more question than alarm.

And that was all that saved Chee-ho. The men suddenly flashed; loud reports shattered the morning's calm, and two of the pheasants began flopping about on the ground, while the rest cried in fright. That was all Chee-ho needed to see. He ran at top speed for several yards and took to the air with a great kah-kah-kah and beat of new-found wingpower as more blasts sounded behind him.

When the survivors gathered in a berry thicket across the river, only six of the original ten remained. Without hesitation, Chee-ho had sought cover. His lesson had been learned in one burst of renascent instinct—men were enemies. Already memories of the friendly people at the college were leaving him. Henceforth he was on his own.

Toward sundown, when his flock had finished feeding, Chee-ho decided they must roost in a stand of young redwood trees near the river. A trail resembling a tunnel led through a tangle of berry bushes beneath the trees. This gave an impression of shelter which the pheasants welcomed. They had no way of knowing that this runway was used by all manner of wild animals, ranging from raccoons and otters about the stream to bobcats and foxes from the woods and hills in back.

The little band chattered to and fro in the covered pathway for a time but finally hopped up into the branches of a chosen tree. Here they arranged themselves about the trunk, some fifteen feet above ground. They could have gone higher, since the redwood stood some seventy feet, but they never had roosted even this high before.

Just at dusk an owl hooted in an alder thicket near by. Newly awakened fears gripped the flock. Two of them descended to the ground and hid in the runway, while the other four huddled closer to the tree trunk above. Chee-ho stayed in the tree, since he felt it was safer to roost above ground. But he was beginning to realize that enemies threatened everywhere in this new habitat.

The wisdom of Chee-ho's decision was proved early in the night. The pheasants in the tree were awakened by the flapping and terrified cries of their two brood mates in the runway below. One of these dashed blindly into the night and flew away—never to be seen again. The other's cries suddenly ceased—to be followed by the gruesome crunching of bones as a bobcat settled to its kill.

When dawn flared over the hills, four pheasants huddled against the redwood's trunk—all that remained after less than twenty-four hours of freedom. Chee-ho was nervous. He had had a disturbed and wakeful night, and felt that when he went to roost again, he must seek a higher level. The survivors had been too close to last night's killing.

More and more, Chee-ho sensed the presence of death and enemies about him, nor was he ever to know another hour of full relaxation. His sheltered upbringing at the college was forgotten. Henceforth, life was primitive, stark, a battle for survival, with no quarter for fools and weaklings. But he had much to learn.

At a signal from Chee-ho, the four pheasants took off abruptly from their roosting place, instead of descending to the ground. Down toward a pool on the river they glided, seeking their morning thirst-quencher. A man sitting beside a fishing rod whipped out a target pistol. The motion caught Chee-ho's eye, and he sheered away with a harsh kak-kak-kak. Two of his flock followed him. The other, a brown-colored pullet, ignored them and alighted beside the water. A volley of cracks tore the early-morning quiet, and she pitched into the water, flopping and bleeding.

The remaining three pheasants left the river and flew across meadow and field for a quarter mile. Then, wings tiring, they dropped to the ground. Food abounded everywhere—grasses, seeds, insects—but they had formed the habit of drinking water before their morning feed, and water they wanted. They were walking through grass higher than themselves, uncertain and confused, when a monstrous animal rose to its feet in front of them. They took to their wings with a chatter of fright—while a cow, satisfied that the rustling portended nothing that might harm her calf, began to browse.

It was on this flight that Chee-ho spotted a small stream at the entrance to a side valley connecting with Mad River. He banked with a cluck of command and coasted down to it. And there they drank. There also they found food, while a field of hay up the valley tempted them to explore further. Before long, Chee-ho noticed a half-dozen fir trees on a hillock and investigated them by circling about them several times. Here seemed the right place to stay. He was beginning to feel satisfied.

A low fog had rolled in from the sea late the day before, but as morning wore on it broke and the sun shone through, watery at first, but becoming brighter and warmer toward midday. Their crops filled with a delicious variety of food, the three pheasants, under Chee-ho's leadership, retreated into the fir trees for a siesta. More and more, Chee-ho was feeling adjusted to this location. Here would be a sheltered roosting place, away from the hills or deep forest. And from it they could see anything approaching from any direction.

Not that Chee-ho thought all this out—rather, his instincts, awakening more with each hour, told him this was good. Thus came the pheasants to Lindsey Creek valley.

And here also they found a friend, for the ranch owner was delighted. Strict orders were issued, and everyone stayed away from the broad central field in the creek bottoms for a time, while the owner went out into the area after dark and spread generous portions of wheat upon the ground. Before long, the pheasants learned that bountiful wheat was forthcoming at the same place every morning. And so, one morning when it was not there, they stood about craning their necks like a neglected flock of chickens, seemingly indignant at the omission.

When a man hove into sight, they flew back into their fir-tree hideout to watch. From there, they saw him spread wheat upon the ground and go away. This awakened dim associations from their past, and before a week was done, they eagerly awaited the man's arrival. Thus a wise rancher accomplished his purpose—and no longer had to go down to the big field at night.

Chee-ho alone retained his mistrust of mankind. His brother and sister accepted this new and semidomestic situation as their just due and settled happily into its routine. Forgotten were their recent experiences with guns, since they had not been hit, and firearms no longer sounded in their vicinity.

On the far side of the narrow valley, outside of the ranch's boundaries, the situation was not so idyllic. A road skirted the base of the hills, and here a colony of transient people had settled by squatters' rights amid tar-paper shacks, dingy trailers, dogs, and general disarray. Over them towered the redwoods, while living water sang beside them and ferns and flowers carpeted the ground. But environment was lost upon these people. Its beauties meant nothing. They felt only that this countryside owed them a living.

Consequently, when a sharp-eyed member of their camp spied the pheasants flying to and fro over the creek bottoms, they made plans.

A growing tension was developing between Chee-ho and his lone brother. The mating urge was in the air, and they had but one pullet between them. During the third week of their residence in Lindsey Creek valley, matters came to a climax.

The two cocks had been eyeing each other with increasing hostility all day, and when roosting time came, Chee-ho asserted himself. In a brief but bitter battle, aided by his sharp spurs, he drove the other cock away from the roosting tree and settled himself on their usual branch with the pullet beside him. The loser sought another tree in the fir hillock—and it was there the jacklighters found him.

Chee-ho and the pullet were awakened by a light beam searching through the fir copse. They huddled together, tense and ready to fly—when a crashing blast deafened their ears and echoed against the hills. They took off into the darkness, while their late brother trickled through the branches and thumped onto the ground. Up by the ranch house on the hill, headlights turned on, and a jeep started for the field pell-mell. But the marauders scuttled away in the darkness with their spoil.

Chee-ho flew blindly over the creek bottoms, with the pullet following. Had it been a moonlit night, they might have had a chance. But in the pitch dark, with even the stars blotted out by an incoming fog, they were helplessly blind. Finally a barn rose before them, and they tumbled, scratching and flopping, onto its sloping roof. They groped their way to the roof top and settled there, terrified and confused. Instinct told Chee-ho that this was not the right place, but instinct could go no farther without eyes to help.

About a half hour before dawn, a soundless thing descended from the darkness above and momentarily enveloped both pheasants in silken-down wingbeats. Chee-ho cried out in terror, leaped down the roofside, and flew away. In the blackness behind him, a steel-strong beak severed the pullet's life cord as a great horned owl made his kill.

Flying frantically, Chee-ho crashed head on into a clump of alders, slid halfway down a tree trunk, and wedged in a tangle of dead branches. And there he stayed until dawn, flaring over the hills, brought sight to his eyes. He was the only pheasant remaining in Lindsey Creek valley now.

As summer swung into full bloom, Chee-ho attained the splendor of a cock pheasant's maturity. Up and down a thousand acres of choice feeding land he paraded, monarch of his realm, and protected by a vigilant friend. Wheat was set out for him, which he continued to eat. He had returned to his original roosting copse after an apprehensive night in the hills. All seemed well with his life now, except that he was lonely.

Summer merged colorfully into fall, and as the days shortened, rains came to Lindsey Creek valley. The stream rose and partially flooded the already dampened meadow and marsh lands. Nights turned cold, and ground mists lay over the lower fields. Long ago, mankind had learned that these vapors were unhealthy. Early-day cabins had been abandoned, and the present owners lived on higher

Wayne Trimm

ground toward the head of the valley. But Chee-ho had no way of knowing this.

The November moon was in its apogee, and the days and nights were filled with the calls of migrating birds on their way south, when Chee-ho began to develop a "pip." At first, this would disappear during the day, especially if a thin sunlight struggled through the clouds and fog. But toward evening, when the chill vapors began to rise, it would come back. He would awaken at night half strangling; and, instead of coming down to feed on his daily wheat ration when the rancher brought it, he began to stay in his roosting place until midmorning. He was feeling more and more poorly and was losing weight.

When the rancher heard Chee-ho's pipping, he went into the fir copse to investigate. Chee-ho allowed the man to approach within twenty yards before taking wing, and then he flew sluggishly to the first convenient landing place. The man went away shaking his head. Next morning, Chee-ho's wheat had a druggy taste, and he refused to eat it at all. Thereafter, he became increasingly thin and bedraggled.

Several mornings later, after an exceptionally bad night, Chee-ho found he could not see through one of his eyes. It had swelled shut. He remained in his fir copse most of the day, gasping and shivering.

That night, the big pheasant could scarcely breathe, and when day dawned his other eye was watering so badly that its vision was dimmed. Chee-ho clung weakly to his perch and, for the first time, did not leave his roosting place all day. When night came, his breath began to rattle. Toward morning he fell to the ground.

It was there the rancher found him, cold and apparently dead. He picked up the emaciated bird and swore. Chee-ho was too far gone to pip, but he opened his beak and gave a faint gasp.

Moments later, the jeep was bounding down the road, with Chee-ho wrapped in burlap beside the driver.

The professor and his students were doing their morning chores about their rearing pens and trout hatchery when the jeep clattered into the game-management yard. The professor made a quick diagnosis.

"Just plain roup," he said. "There was a time when we wouldn't have had a chance, but perhaps with antibiotics —anyhow, we'll try. Look, it's one of our birds. Here's our leg band."

Chee-ho was too near death to recover rapidly, but before a week went by his bad eye had reopened and its vision was clearing. With it came a returning appetite and, with that, a renewed interest in life.

In a few more days he was transferred to an outdoor pen, near which was an enclosure containing a dozen pheasant pullets. Possibly it was the natural interest of a male in the opposite sex, more probably it was a leftover from his thwarted mating urge of the past spring; but Chee-ho soon was spending much of his time on the side nearest the pullets' enclosure, watching and occasionally chuckling.

The rancher was amused when he visited the college to see how his bird was faring. "Just a wolf in pheasant's feathers," he said.

The professor smiled. "He's all right," he said. "Say— how would you like to take this big fellow and a selected harem up to your ranch this coming spring and raise pheasants?"

The rancher was delighted. "But why the harem?" he asked. "Don't these fellows mate for life, like eagles?"

"Oh no, they're as polygamous as chickens. One rooster will do for a fair little flock. In fact, they are distantly related to our domestic fowl."

"Well, I'll fix them a closed-in yard so that bobcats, owls, poachers, and other varmints can't get at 'em. Perhaps they'll get a break this time."

"But turn them loose before actual nesting time," advised the professor. "They'll be used to your surroundings by then and will stay close to home."

Thus, at winter's end, Chee-ho found himself master of a tidy half dozen pullets in a spacious enclosure on the Lindsey Creek ranch, high and dry above the damp lands below. Never had he felt so sure of himself. His glossy plumage shone in the warming sunlight, and his high-pitched crow gave notice and warning to any and all males, pheasant or domestic. For this was his property, his palace, wherein he, and he alone, was sultan. And his flock concurred.

One balmy spring morning, the professor came up from the college. For a time, he studied the increasingly restless seekings of the hen pheasants. No longer did they follow their lord and master about. Rather, each seemed more interested in seeking a secluded place for herself. The flock spirit, which had distinguished them at first, now seemed gone. Nor did Chee-ho appear interested in keeping them together any longer. He acted somewhat bored and spent some bit of his time sunning himself alone and eating. He watched the men with cool eyes, and when they opened the door of the enclosure, he was the first to leave.

By nightfall, the hen pheasants were scattered in a half dozen different directions, and each, with that sureness of instinct which makes their kind revert to the wild when released, had found a haven for herself and the clutches of eggs soon to be laid. Under tangled berry bushes, in thickets, and out into the hayfields they went—but always the chosen nesting place was on the ground, well concealed.

Chee-ho's work for the season was done. To the hens went the duty of sitting on their eggs for some twenty-three days and then leading the new broods through all the pitfalls and perils of their start in life. To the hens went the worries of protecting their chicks against the watchful eyes of a hungry and hostile world . . . to bring the survivors through to the fall molt if Providence decreed.

To all of this Chee-ho was insensitive. He was free. The hens no longer interested him. Once again, all of Lindsey Creek valley belonged to him, and he gloried in it. Daily he returned to the ranch to pick up the ever present bounty of grain—a thing his hens would not do until later. Daily his range grew, and soon he had chosen an oak tree on the dangerous far side of the valley, outside the ranch, for his roosting place.

It was there a prowling youth spied him one morning at dawn. The crack of a .22 rifle did not carry halfway to the ranch house, but the bullet sped true. A vicious, split-nosed thing, it shattered Chee-ho's head into splinters and ribbons —which, if it had to happen, was merciful, for he never knew what hit him.

But the life stream of Chee-ho carries on. His children and grandchildren squabble cheerfully over the endless supply of food in the ranch yard; while his widowed hens, under new masters long since, nest ever farther into the uplands of Lindsey Creek valley, even as do their daughters. True, the breed is increasing slowly, since casualties run high.

Now and then the rancher remembers the big cock pheasant that started his flock; nor does he relax his vigilance against marauders, whether two-legged, four-footed, or winged.

And so Chee-ho is vindicated, even though his body went into an inglorious stew pot. His actuality is as ever living as the redwoods . . . to earth reborn.

On Matters of Strategy

Big Wapiti was boss-bull of an elk herd that resided amid the age-old forests of the north-coastal Redwood Empire. His headquarters—if such they could be called—were at Plateau State Park.

Here, rigorously protected by park rangers and game wardens, these survivors of a once-abundant species had multiplied and prospered. So much so, in fact, that not a few kill-hungry individuals had been after the state to declare an elk-hunting season.

To Wapiti, life was pleasant and no more than routinely eventful. His nine-hundred-pound bulk, combined with wisdom and pugnacity, gave him mastery over his herd. While benevolent discipline sufficed as a rule, it was necessary each year in his line of duty to put aspiring young bulls in their places. But this was normal procedure, and he would not have had it otherwise. Thus he remained assured.

In a natural clearing that comprised several hundred acres—and which was bisected by a state highway—Wapiti and his followers spent much of their time. Not only was food abundant here, but the rangers set out additional provender as the time of year might warrant.

The one factor to which Wapiti never had become quite reconciled was that highway—a barren path over which monsters of assorted sizes roared back and forth at all hours of the day and night.

Often these unwelcome things would stop and people would emerge from them to stare and gabble. After a time, they would disappear, always to be replaced by others. And they were not to be trusted. Now and then a gun would shoot—which would cause the hurried arrival of a park ranger, together with much additional gabbling.

Worst of all—when Wapiti or any of his herd wanted to go from the coast side of the forest to its inland side, it was necessary to cross this reeking path of the monsters. This they would do at top speed; but even so, the elk were in danger from the swift-running intruders.

While accidents were few, there had been occasions when monsters would attack an elk with disastrous results. True, the monster would be wounded so that other monsters would appear and drag it away. But the elk that had been attacked was taken away also—never to be seen again.

And so, Wapiti's cow elk made certain that each year's young were carefully prepared against this path of peril. Nor were any allowed to cross it until they were large enough not only to travel at speed, but to leap the fences on each side with ease and agility.

From Plateau Park clearing westward to the ocean's shore, the forests were an elk sanctum. Here almost no fences were found, and roads were few. While monsters from the main path ventured into this area at times, their progress was slow and they seemed out of their element. But experience had taught the herd to avoid these menaces wherever they traveled the narrow paths between the trees. They were more apt to disgorge men with guns than those out in the open among others of their kind.

Also, there were certain sections of the forest, farther removed, where men, monsters, and destruction seemed to belong. Here, with a great deal of noise, they tore down trees and dragged them away.

This was another area of danger, and Wapiti's herd avoided it for most of the year. During the rain time, it appeared quiet and deserted—but even then a stray man with a gun might be there. To the elk, that situation seemed a disease—an abnormality beyond their ken which bore watching at all times.

This particular summer, the situation was rather less to Wapiti's liking than at any time before. Not only were more men and monsters swarming everywhere, but one young bull elk, now in his early prime, refused to stay in his place. Twice Wapiti had administered beatings to this recalcitrant individual, but young Upstart was built of durable material and came back for more.

While November's rutting moon was some months removed, both bulls knew a battle to the finish was certain to occur. Wapiti was feeling increasingly restless and angry. He was at the peak of his prime—the climax. Another year would see him about the same, while Upstart was still in his ascendancy. Moreover, the obtruder stayed constantly in sight instead of keeping his distance, as other bachelors had learned from Wapiti to do. To the boss bull this rivalry had become a matter of strategy, wherein the end justified the means.

One afternoon, when Upstart had approached somewhat closer to forbidden ground than the rules specified, Wapiti took issue with him again. But this time, when the younger bull stood his ground, Wapiti appeared to hesitate. He turned away, tossing his head heavy with antlers new grown from springtime. The opposition became aggressive. Still Wapiti gave ground, and when Upstart charged, he ran away. That did it. Athrob with triumph and self-confidence, the young bull took after him—nor heeded where the chase might lead. Straight for the highway fence went Wapiti, and over it in one sailing leap. And then he stopped without crossing—a thing he never had done before. Upstart landed beside him, and for moments the two animals fenced and sparred almost in the midst of traffic.

Startled automobile drivers squee'd their tires and swerved wildly. That a pile-up did not occur was a miracle. Twice, Wapiti maneuvered his opponent onto the highway itself. By now all the monsters had stopped and were braying and hooting. This was not to either bull elk's liking. As one animal, they sailed over the far-side fence and raced across Plateau Park's clearing toward the woods.

Still Wapiti did not stop. With Upstart in ardent pursuit, he fled into the forest. There he started down a trail with long-legged strides that took him faster than most horses could gallop—straight for one of those places where men and monsters were tearing down trees.

Minutes later, an astounded logging crew stopped work to gape at a pair of bull elk that sprinted through their operations. The one being chased kept more to cover than the other, they noted, but they did not understand. To them, it was all a mystery.

To Wapiti, however, it was not. For the only time in his life, he wanted to hear the report of a gun—but, as so often occurs when a desired event is sought, it did not happen.

Again the two elk plunged into the woods and out of men's sight. Halfway back to the park clearing, Wapiti suddenly faced about and, without preliminary, charged into Upstart at full tilt. The pursuer was taken by surprise. Before he had time to get set, he was bowled off his feet and, while struggling to rise, received a rough goring.

Had it been rutting season, the battle would have been to the end. But this encounter lacked final incentive, despite Wapiti's connivance. Upstart finally regained his feet, and the two bulls crashed head on with much grunting and rattling of antlers.

Now Wapiti the experienced had the situation under control. One of Upstart's antlers had been partly splintered, and he was bleeding from several hoof slashes. Also, the younger bull was upset from the perilous chases through which he had been led.

Abruptly, Upstart turned and started to run away. But Wapiti was not satisfied. Straight for the Plateau Park clearing he drove his antagonist, turning him every time he tried

Wayne Trimm

to dodge off course. Wapiti knew what he wanted. The rest of the herd must witness Upstart's humiliation and defeat, that its leader's prestige might be sustained.

And so it was. With a concluding burst of speed, Wapiti drove the pretender across most of the clearing, and then back into the woods, where he rejoined his charges, snorting and blowing to show his mastery.

The rangers had witnessed part of the Wapiti-Upstart fracas, and its implications were clear—especially the highway incident. For its own good, the elk herd must be thinned down or divided; even though the park personnel abhorred the idea of a hunt with all of its repercussions.

As a result, while Wapiti reigned blissfully and unchallenged, and Upstart stayed out of sight, correspondence passed back and forth. The head office pondered the problem and, in due time, made up its collective mind. Elk were needed in a certain rugged and remote sector of northeastern California, it seemed. Ergo, since Plateau Park had elk in excess, two projects could be handled as one.

Wapiti and his faithful were beyond such man-inspired doings. All they knew was that their tenancy of the land was rudely disturbed one morning when several horsemen galloped into the park clearing, whooping, and waving strange things in the air.

Now the elk never had seen cowboys in action, but these persons' presence lacked something in appeal. Unsavory doings seemed afoot. As one animal, Wapiti and his herd took to the forest, outdistancing these trespassers as jack rabbits running from bull terriers.

Once amid the trees, their safety was assured, since no lasso could reach them. Nor could the cowboys drive them into the open. They scattered throughout the woods in indignation, and the angriest of the herd was Wapiti. Here was another affront to his supremacy, and the urge was upon him to return and give battle to these invaders of his domain.

During the night the herd returned to their clearing and, when they found the situation quiet, bedded down. Next morning, however, the enemies on horses returned. This time, they tried to cut the elk off from escape into the woods. But the area involved was too large and the herd too swift. After much galloping about and dust raising, the elk again reached sanctuary intact. Thereafter, they became more wary than ever.

For two days and a night, the herd stayed away from Plateau Park clearing. Then again they returned—only to be chased to and fro and back into the forest again when daylight came.

By now, Wapiti was in a towering rage. The morale of his charges was suffering, and, as their leader, he had to do something about it. Upstart had stayed out of sight during the recent furor, but Wapiti knew his would-be successor was not far away.

It was midmorning after the elk herd's third rout when Wapiti strode into Plateau Park clearing in all of his incensed dignity. He snorted, shook his head, and pawed the ground in challenge. But for a time, nothing happened.

Then, in a matter of moments, galloping horses appeared from several directions. Wapiti lowered his head and charged. But, while he could outrun the horses, he could not scatter them, and he was quickly encircled.

A lasso dropped onto his antlers, another caught a foreleg, while still another looped around the opposite hind leg. And now the cowboys knew what to do and how to do it. The job was not easy, but in seconds they had an enraged and struggling bull elk securely trussed and all but choked. Even then, Wapiti was not frightened. Rather he was outraged that such an indignity to his person could have occurred.

As matters stood, Wapiti's capture was scant triumph. Four days of galloping and dust raising plus costly long-distance travel had netted the cowboys one elk. And now it looked as if the herd would stay away from the clearing indefinitely. No one was especially happy.

And then the blow descended. Wapiti found himself released in a small, high-sided pen, after having been ignominously shoved aboard a noisy monster and hauled a short distance. Bonds loosed, he sprang to his feet—and in minutes had battered his way through the wooden fence slats, despite all efforts to contain him. With a final scattering of debris, he took to the forest. And such was his speed that recapture en route was out of the question. No one was happy now at all.

A number of spectators from a nearby state park camp had been watching the fun. Now, one of them approached the man in charge and asked: "Do them elk like apples?" He was assured that they did.

"Well," the spectator continued, "why don't you set out some apples with micky finns in 'em then?—you know, sleepin' pills."

He was informed a bit tartly that such procedure was not "policy." The visitor shrugged his shoulders and walked away. But he had started more than he knew. Mind was overriding matter. Strategy was afoot. . . .

Next night, the cowboys with their trailers and paraphernalia left as unostentatiously as the proverbial Arabs. Once again, correspondence with the head office got under way.

Back with his herd, a bruised and angry Wapiti was in no mood to take anything from man, horse, or elk. He scoured the woods, looking to pick a fight with Upstart, but that prudent animal had made himself scarce.

Thereafter, it was decreed that the herd stay clear of Plateau Park clearing entirely. Food of the kind they always had known was set out in the customary places, but it remained untouched.

Two weeks passed. Gradually Wapiti's anger had subsided and, since neither he nor his cohorts had seen any

horsemen about, they began returning at night for a meal—
and leaving before dawn.

One night, they found a box of apples scattered about,
and ate the succulent fruit with relish. Next night, no food
was there. They lingered hopefully until morning. Sure
enough, the familiar rangers came out with grain as usual,
and a half-truce was established. For a week this continued,
until the herd was staying in the clearing for much of the
day.

Wapiti, while still wary and watchful, had relaxed the
rules by now. Had so much as one horseman appeared on
the scene, returning confidence would have been shattered.
But, to every appearance, life had settled back to its pre-
cowboy tenor as summer waned, and when another box of
delicious red apples was scattered about one morning,
every elk in the herd ate its share greedily.

At first, Wapiti was puzzled. The world about him seemed
unsteady. A cow elk bumped into him, herself unsteady,
and all but knocked him off his feet. Something was very
wrong. In sudden panic, Wapiti tried to run for the woods,
but his consciousness was dimming. Try though he might,
his legs would not obey, and he wanted only to sleep.

To the last, he fought this cloud of numbness that was
enveloping him—but finally blacked out. He had gotten
farther from the scene than any of the others, but he was
down for the count.

Next thing Wapiti knew, he was securely trussed and lying
on his side in what seemed a worse prison than the narrow
pen from which he had broken free before. He was weak
and felt sick. Nor could he move about. They were taking
no chances with him this time. Several others of the herd
were packed in beside him, and they too were helpless.
Something beyond his comprehension had happened.

Outside his prison pen, men were gabbling and shouting
excitedly, while the well-known sound and smell of gasoline
engines rent the air. Wapiti closed his eyes with a groan

and, for the first time in a free and untrammeled lifetime, awaited the worst.

And the worst was not long in coming. The trailer, in which he and the several others were confined, jerked into motion with a roar. The unhappy animals were jounced about, demoralized and upset.

Be it said to the credit of the rangers—they handled the trucks with meticulous care, while their bound captives were bedded atop deep straw to make them as comfortable as possible. But time was of the essence now. A several hours' journey was ahead, nor could the elk be watered while en route. This entailed no especial hardship, however. And it was the best the men could do under the circumstances.

As the miles whisked beneath them, the captive elk in the several truck-trailer rigs gradually calmed down. Fear of the unknown had been supplanted by resignation. Even Wapiti ceased his struggling and grunting. The straw was ample and not too uncomfortable, while the motion of the vehicle no longer seemed to threaten.

New odors filtered through to them, despite the smell of engine exhausts. Reaction set in, and some of them dozed briefly. A stop to take on fuel brought them to alarmed wakefulness again, but when motion was resumed the animals subsided.

Late that afternoon, the convoy of trucks arrived at Elk Valley, a carefully selected area in the upland of the Sierra which once had contained numbers of their species. A couple of acres of ground had been enclosed with a high, strong wire fence, with a releasing pen opening into the main corral. The job had been well planned.

Tired and perspiring men trundled the elk one at a time into the pen, released their bonds, and let them scramble to their feet and enter the corral at will. So smoothly did the work progress that, within minutes, the herd of a dozen animals had been freed. The last to be turned loose was

Wapiti, who, glad of release, trotted out into the corral and rejoined his flock. Not included in their number was Upstart, since the park personnel had selected their "transplants" with care and did not want two feuding bulls together.

The trucks and men left, while the elk explored the enclosure and stared at the surrounding territory. A small spring bubbled inside the corral, while food was there in abundance. Before long they drank and, later, started feeding. In this new and unknown environment, they were content to stay close to one another, and had no desire to escape. Nor could the most agile of them leap the ten-foot fence.

Morning found them in good fettle and becoming restive. A truck called briefly and unloaded more food. They crowded into the farthest corner away from it, but felt no especial fear. Rather, its presence was, in a way, reassuringly familiar.

Wapiti alone was imbued with a desire to start exploring the new land outside. The small but lush valley, guarded on all sides by high mountains, smelled of any number of inviting things. True, more food was in the corral than he and his companions could possibly eat, but the outside meadows looked more enticing. He did not attempt to leap the fence that contained him, but began trying to butt his way free. After a series of efforts, he gave that up. This was unlike any barrier he had encountered before.

On the second morning of the elk's confinement, a man arrived quietly on foot. Prior warned, he had tethered his horse out of sight in the nearby woods in order not to panic the enclosed herd. He and Wapiti looked at each other with perhaps a degree of understanding, although all the elk kept their distance.

The man's garb was familiar. He made no sudden motions, but watched the herd for some time. In spite of himself, Wapiti felt little hostility or fear. In some manner, this man seemed in accord with the elk, rather than an enemy.

After a time the man left, and Wapiti noticed that an opening had appeared in the fence. Cautiously he approached this gate and inspected the exitway. Nothing seemed amiss. He stepped outside.

Then, in sudden suspicion of he knew not what, he re-entered the corral. But nothing untoward happened. Again he stepped outside, while others of the herd approached the opening with combined uneasiness and curiosity.

Within minutes all but a timid one or two had left the corral. Food in abundance had been left outside, but they were so amply fed that, for the present, this did not interest them.

Other things did, though, and for most of the day the elk circled within sight of the enclosure investigating, smelling, and looking. The area was strangely quiet. No monsters raced and roared about, nor did they see any more human beings. Toward evening, they returned to the vicinity of the corral and fed, but none re-entered its confines.

Next morning, when a light truck arrived, dumped grain, and left, they retreated temporarily into the woods but did not run.

Thus, in a few weeks' time, the elk herd became accustomed to their new environment. The timber was smaller—mostly fir instead of lofty redwoods—and the air smelled different; for this was a land of high altitude to which considerable snow would come. But it was a land of peace and quiet and, instinctively, the elk felt in harmony with it—even as others of their kind who had lived there in the past.

Now, however, they were as rigorously protected as they had been in the redwood forests near the seacoast, while the rangers would see to it that food and shelter were supplied during winters to come.

To Wapiti, this had become an accepted abode, although it was a more primitive environment than the busy Redwood

Empire. He smelled bears and cougars and knew these would threaten the herd, while they had still to experience the rigors of the Sierra winter. But the ingrained ruggedness of his species could survive that. And the noise and odors of mankind were gone.

With the approach of the rutting moon, the big bull elk knew he was lord of his domain as never before. His range was increasing until it embraced the length of Elk Valley and up into the river's headwaters. And so Wapiti was content.

Father Klamath's Children

There is only one Klamath River—that far-flung source of Indian lore which rises in the fastness of the Siskiyou and Coast Range mountains and riffles through the heart of the northern Redwood Empire to its meeting with the sea.

A perilous river it is. And the Indians will tell you that when Father Klamath goes on the warpath, none may stand in his way. Puny mankind, who dared build too near his bastions, has had its chattels obliterated like toys in the sand when the floods came. And others even more foolhardy, who flaunted his white-maned wrath in impotent boats, have been swallowed in his maw, never to reappear.

But—the Indians also will tell you—Father Klamath is a benign life source from whose largess their ancestors had been endowed with strength and sustenance from time beyond the memory of legends.

For the Klamath River is an enduring Elysium for the fish tribes—from great sturgeon, whose weight may run into hundreds of pounds, to silvery shad introduced by mankind.

Greatest, though, are the king, or chinook, salmon, and the steelhead-rainbow trout—those royal game fish whose legions come in from the sea during their spawning sagas; while the steelhead's young populate the river with growing trout the year round. Thus Father Klamath is that mecca whence faithful fishermen make their pilgrimage ere they are done.

And so to the story . . . Late one fall, a pair of king-chinook salmon, actuated by an urge beyond mankind's ability to fathom, had pushed their way up the Klamath's sweep to the headwaters of the Little Shasta River in Siski-you County—a tributary where they first had known life over four years before.

There, battered and torn, they had excavated a nest, or redd, in a riffle of coarse sand, and had spawned and fertilized some five-thousand reddish, pea-sized eggs. Then, with final dying effort, they covered their cache with several inches of sand. By now, their once-powerful tails were in shreds, while their blackened bodies were eaten with sores and fungus-infected white patches.

Life's work done, the parent salmon then had obeyed nature's decree and rejoined their ancestors from uncounted ages before.

Now, however, spring had come to the Siskiyou-Klamath domain. Cold, angry waters had subsided and were warm-ing with promise of life to be renewed. Beneath sheltering sand of the Little Shasta egg-redd—chosen with unerring instinct for texture, so that oxygen-bearing water could penetrate but not wash away—life was stirring. The salmon eggs that had lain seemingly dormant through winter's cold now showed tiny eyes through semitransparent shells. Oc-casionally these eyes would move as the developing fish shifted within their confinement.

The odd-appearing mites that emerged from these king-chinook eggs could not less have resembled the great silvery fish that a final few of them were destined to be. They were a scant five eighths of an inch long, jelly-opaque, and tailless, with conspicuous eyes. The yolk sac from their incubating egg was still attached to their bodies. This would furnish nourishment for their beginning days of life.

Prompted by an instinct as old as their species, they wriggled their way up through the loose sand a fraction of an inch at a time, taking a day or more to reach the surface. And there the hazards of life began.

To all predators in the stream, from water bugs and small

fish to snakes and frogs, the baby salmon were easy prey. While almost every egg in the redd had hatched, perhaps half of the ensuing young were eaten within a week of their reaching the surface. And this was early in the season, before too many enemies were about.

One young king-chinook had taken longer to hatch than most of his brood, and he seemed somewhat larger than the rest. Once out of the egg, he worked his way to the surface rather more quickly than average—and almost at once encountered danger.

A fingerling steelhead-rainbow trout—his distant half cousin—made for him in leisurely sureness. A kingfisher swooped, and in the ensuing upset, young king-chinook was overlooked. But the newly hatched salmon was not designed for propulsion in his tailless form. After a prolonged four-inch swim, he came to rest on his side.

He had moved far enough, however, that the current picked him up and carried him several feet before depositing him in a slow-turning eddy behind a rock. And there he lay in quiet, his downstream journey under way.

Newly hatched though young Chinook was, that microcosm from the Infinite which comprised his life spark already felt the summons to migrate downstream. Other species of salmon, as well as steelhead-rainbow trout, may stay in fresh water up to the age of two years—to furnish sport for amateurs. But the king-chinook heads for the mother sea almost as soon as it is able to move, nor delays en route regardless of the journey's length.

So it was in the case of Chinook and his siblings. Before a week had elapsed, they were on their way down the Little Shasta toward the Klamath River. But an ever increasing number of enemies were exacting toll as the new-born salmon began their hegira.

By now, Chinook was taking shape as a fish. The yolk sac of his first few days had been absorbed, his tail was growing in earnest, and he was feeding voraciously on algae and microscopic organisms in the water. Each day was bringing progress and growth.

Time and again he was threatened by enemies. That he had not been eaten at first was pure good fortune. Now, however, his instincts were sharpening and he was becoming ever more alert with each experience.

And young Chinook had basic reason to sharpen his faculties, for the survival rate of his species is so low, that once mankind upsets its rate of return by excessive fishing pressure both at sea and in the rivers, its numbers can only diminish.

For instance—out of a possible five thousand king-chinooks that hatch in a river redd, perhaps three or four may return as adult fish to carry on their kind. The rest—so far as scientists are able to ascertain—do not survive, so heavy are the odds against them.

Thus, if a sizeable number of maturing salmon are taken before they can spawn, the balance tips against them and the law of diminishing returns takes effect. And each successive generation that is partly depleted before spawning leaves ever fewer to make up the deficit. Two or three may return to their birthplaces, where a minimum of three or four should.

Dedicated men have done their best in salmon hatcheries where, in theory, enough young salmon are saved from the perils of the streams to get a larger number to sea than would occur in natural propagation. But even this seems a losing battle. Once nature's cycle is disturbed, there seems to be no mending it.

Young Chinook's progress down the Little Shasta to its main stream and thence into the Klamath River was now swift. Those fast-flowing waters led to the place where his instincts commanded him to go. And such was the grip of his drive, inherited from ancestors who first ventured into fresh water aeons ago, that he could only obey blindly. Except for the first and last chapters of their lives, king-

chinook salmon are salt-water fish. Therein they differ from
sea-run trout, who seem able to enter and leave fresh water
about as they choose.

The main Klamath River was swollen from spring rains
and melting snows. Its very opaqueness as it roared down
mountain gorges was a protection to Chinook, en route to
the sea. Food was abundant in the roily water, and he
picked up sustenance on the run as he was rushed from
riffle to rapid. The very river itself seemed eager to co-
operate in his descent to the Pacific.

Chinook was over a month old, nearly two inches long,
and several times his original bulk, when he reached the
confluence of the Klamath and Trinity rivers at Weitchpec,
in the Hoopa Indian Reservation. At this point, another
great stream united with Father Klamath, and the combined rivers' size was almost doubled for the remaining
forty-odd-mile dash to the sea.

To Chinook, the Trinity River's advent served only to
enhance his downstream flight. Now and then, in a comparatively calm pocket, he might encounter others of his
kind, but this meant nothing either to him or them. A week
later, he was at the edge of tidewater, near the Klamath
River mouth.

By now, the river had quieted, as if loath to merge its
freedom into the finality of the sea. And here the water
teemed with enemies. Voracious cutthroat trout, schooled
by ages of experience, were on the hunt. Thousands of
young king-chinooks who had survived the downstream
hazards now met their end.

And here the schooling instinct first asserted itself as
harried survivors banded together and made their final
dash into salt water. Death awaited those who hesitated in
the turning tides. Death tore at their thinning numbers as
they left the river. Death pursued them out into the sea
itself where, finally, the beleaguered little schools found
refuge of sorts in seaweed beds.

The calm, salty Pacific was complete contrast to the rushing rivers Chinook had known in his brief life, but ancestral background made him at once adaptable. The seaweed beds swarmed with all manner of life, from predatory bass and ling cod to swarms of tiny crustaceans that hovered in gnatlike clouds around the weed fronds and furnished provender for the young salmon.

An occasional cutthroat trout still hunted through the weed beds, for these speckled gamesters will move back and forth from river to sea at will. But so abundant was forage of all kinds in this haven that Chinook and his kind were comparatively safe—although the battle for survival would never cease.

Chinook's growth while on his downstream migration had been ample to take him through. Now, however, he was surrounded by food in superabundance, and nature was urging him to grow with all possible speed. He stayed consistently gorged. Each day was bringing additional size. Within weeks, he had become a four-incher as his metabolism worked overtime to accumulate and assimilate.

By now, the schooling instinct which had asserted itself during the peril at the river mouth had evolved further. Young king-chinooks began banding together more or less permanently and were working their ways both north and south from the area where Father Klamath's flow tinged the sea. But the survivors would return—although some of their number might journey south below Monterey, while others would go as far north as Puget Sound before they returned to the waters of their birth.

For reasons known only to the Creator, Chinook and his immediate school headed south. While all of these young salmon came from some part of the Klamath watershed, they were not necessarily related. In fact, it is quite possible that none of Chinook's original siblings from the Little Shasta redd were among this particular group. Rather, they held together as a common species. Later, they would join other schools of young king-chinooks from the Sacramento, Eel, and Mattole rivers—waters that flowed into the Pacific from California south of the Klamath.

For the first year of their lives, Chinook and his school-fellows stayed reasonably close to shore and the kelp beds. Not only were these areas good protection from enemies, but their food content was high. True, they were harassed by diving birds and all manner of predatory fish, but had they ventured farther out to sea among larger salmon, they would have been eaten by their own kind.

They worked a leisurely way downcoast, where they were joined by others from the more southerly streams. South of Humboldt Bay the cutthroat trout menace no longer occurred, but they had learned by then to avoid stream mouths whence enemies might sally forth.

The start of his second year of life found Chinook a sizeable twelve inches, and inclined to venture into deeper water. By this time, he was off San Francisco Bay entrance where Sacramento River salmon were encountered, and the schools grew in size.

Here, too, when fishing season began, boats were churning above, while shiny lures flashed through the water. Numbers of big salmon fell victim to them, while sea lions were increasingly in evidence. But these cumbersome kill-ers were easily avoided, nor did the lures tempt many of Chinook's generation. They were too small for that.

The start of his third summer at sea found Chinook past two years of age. He had grown to over twenty inches in length and had deepened in his midriff until he weighed better than seven pounds. He was in the ocean off Monterey Bay by now, far south of the Klamath River mouth, which was a fortunate thing.

Certain young salmon males attain "teen-age" maturity at this stage. If they are within reasonable reach of their native waters, they are apt to follow the runs of spawning adults into the rivers. While they are capable of the male function, few of them seem to procreate. Rather, they linger around the spawning redds and make nuisances of themselves trying to eat eggs. They are then known as grilse or, colloquially, jack or chub salmon. Perhaps all-seeing Nature decrees this phenomenon in case of disaster to the older males. No man knows the answer.

This phase might not do especial harm, since the steelhead-rainbows do the same thing without depletion of their species—except for one thing. The sea-run trout survive to return to the Pacific, whereas the grilse salmon succumb to the curse of their tribe and die along with their elders. Thus their premature migration ends in futility. Nature is lavish with life. . . .

Although Chinook felt a slight urge when fall spawning time approached and adult king-chinooks headed for the Sacramento River, he did not want to follow. Older members from the Klamath River watershed whose spawning odyssey was near had turned north some while before, but he had not been aware of their departure.

By late next spring, when Chinook had completed his third year of life, his size had increased greatly. The grilse stage was safely past. A diet of shrimp not only had helped make him a twenty-five pounder, but had reddened his flesh to a point much desired by fishermen and connoisseurs. Likewise, he was consuming quantities of sardines, smelt, and anchovies, while—it must be added—he enjoyed small salmon and steelhead trout if available. He had become a predator, perhaps in justice to earlier hunted days, and life was good.

About this time, he became aware of another salmon—a female—who, for reasons beyond science's ken, he knew came from his Little Shasta watershed. Although he might not see her for days at a time, the two salmon stayed with the same school and were never far apart.

Fishing boats, both sports and commercial, were out on the ocean in numbers as the weather calmed and warmed.

While Chinook had no especial fear of them, he tended to avoid them on the same surmise that he avoided anything large and strange—which included sharks, sea lions, and killer whales. More and more frequently, he witnessed salmon around his own age and size dashing about in distress when the boats were near. And often the sea would be tinged with salmon blood and entrails, which attracted enemies as well as flapping sea gulls. While Chinook was unable to connect cause and effect, still he came to associate such disturbances with boats and avoided them further.

One foggy morning he was cruising near the surface like a silvery torpedo when what appeared to be a wounded sardine flashed past. As a moth is drawn to a flame, Chinook took after it and seized it with a jolt that startled a man in a boat, a hundred yards away.

But this sardine did not act like food. It was hard, like a shell, and it bit into his jaw. More than that—it showed unusual strength and jerked as if trying to escape. Chinook shook his head in sudden anger and tried to swim away. But this peculiar sardine began tugging as no prey he had ever known. Alarmed now, Chinook tried to take off at speed. But the sardine held him back and, pull though he might, he was unable to get under way. His jaw was paining, and, with that pain, Chinook knew he was fighting for his life against an unknown foe.

Wild with fear, he leaped halfway out of water and cut a circle around the boat. Whether he realized by then that the boat had any connection with his fight, no one can say. But he soon saw that it was drawing nearer to him, and his dread increased.

Then abruptly he sounded deep. As he did so, the female salmon from the Little Shasta arrived and swam beside him, apparently aware that something was wrong. She circled about and followed as Chinook was being pumped inexorably to the surface again.

The fisherman's line was strong, and the leader was of

piano wire. Against such a rig, Chinook had no chance. In minutes, he was drawn alongside the boat, still thrashing his broad tail and twisting about, while his follower darted to and fro in consternation.

By all odds of the game, Chinook's life should have ended then and there. But the sportsmen were amateurs. They had "horsed" their big fish instead of playing him until he floated, exhausted. As a result, the triple hook, which had only taken hold with one barb, now held by a shred.

A perspiring angler saw this as Chinook surfaced near the boat. He shouted to his nervous partner to "gaff that fish quick!" As he did, the female salmon broke water alongside Chinook with a splash that threw water in both men's faces. The man with the gaff made an awkward pass that raked a wound across Chinook's back. His partner jerked the heavy pole in near-stampede. The hook tore free. As one fish, Chinook and the female salmon dove out of sight.

Chinook's wound from the gaff hook was superficial, but its lesson was not. Thereafter, he and his companion regarded boats as predatory enemies and shunned them.

In the winter that followed, the school to which Chinook and the female salmon belonged ranged south almost to Morro Rock on the San Luis Obispo County coast, which took them below the southernmost line of the Redwood Empire and to the southerly extension of their species' normal range. They stayed several miles at sea for the most part and found the feeding good. Almost no boats were about.

March's winds were still whipping sea and sky, when a number of the school detached themselves from the main aggregation and started north. Most of them were salmon that were turning four years old at the time. Some were a year or two older, since not all king-chinooks spawn at the four-year mark—although overage fish are in the minority.

Among the northbound group were both Chinook and the female from the Little Shasta. It would be several months before the school reached the Klamath-mouth area, but they were on their way as surely as if they had been trains on rails. Already, nature was preparing their bodies for their rendezvous at the spawning redds. Skeins of roe, with eggs no more than birdshot size, were developing inside the female salmon's fat-lined flanks, while the males' milt glands were swelling.

By now, Chinook was growing into a magnificent forty-pound king salmon, silver-coated, and with that sprinkling of large black spots which distinguishes his tribe. Life surged strongly within him, and he reveled in his strength. He had become the leader of his coterie, for every group of salmon or trout has its number-one member, who seems to feel responsibility for watching over the others.

As the salmon moved farther north, they merged with still more from the Redwood Empire streams. But those who belonged in the Eel, Mattole, and other rivers would leave when the taste of their home waters permeated the sea. And there were some from Oregon who would continue farther north after the Klamath River contingent dropped out.

By the time they were off Cape Mendocino in early summer, their numbers were such that airplane pilots, watching overhead, reported a "huge school" of salmon offshore. Some of the big fish put into the waters around Humboldt Bay entrance, where sports fishermen held forth. Also, fleets of commercial fishing vessels, directed by airplane data, were taking heavy toll. And this had been almost constant from San Francisco north.

By now, Chinook and the queen salmon from the Little Shasta were rarely out of each other's sight. With the scar on Chinook's back as warning, both of them stayed away from all boats and, save for an occasional chase by predators, made the journey without incident.

The first touch of fall was in the air, heralding the Redwood Empire's peace of the giants, when Chinook and his mate-to-be arrived off the Klamath River mouth. Of the thousands that had started for that destination a few months before—both from the north and south—perhaps half had got there safely.

The cutthroat trout that had plagued and slaughtered them when they were babies seeking the sea now fled in terror; for the grown salmon were quite capable of turning the tables if the occasion gave them opportunity. And this had been true from Humboldt Bay's scope northward, as they flanked the heart of the northern Redwood Empire.

But with mankind at the Klamath River, it was a different story. Hordes of small boats were anchored at the river's mouth, just inside the breaker line—with each occupant letting the outflow of the stream whirl his spinner in hopes that an incoming salmon would seize it. Many were the tangle-ups when a hooked fish raced across the lines. Loud were the accusations and threats. And on shore, fisherman were casting elbow-to-elbow in eagerness and hope.

Chinook and his queen-salmon cruised outside the surf in bewilderment. This swarming of mankind was too recent in their evolution for instinct to handle. But they knew what boats meant, and would not enter the river-estuary despite harassment from sea lions.

For two days, they lingered in indecision, while their ancestral call summoned ever more imperatively. Finally, at night, when the situation appeared quiet, they joined a lately arrived group and crossed into the brackish water of Father Klamath's lagoon. Here they milled about for a time and moved into fresh water where they leaped and rolled about to rid themselves of sea lice—a small banjo-shaped parasite that clings beneath their fins at sea, but which lets go and dies in fresh water.

Next morning at break of dawn, boats started bearing down upon them from landings upstream. Without hesitation, Chinook and Queen, followed by a number of others, fled the lagoon into ocean water again, where they sulked throughout the day.

That night was a different story. When darkness brought calm, and others had gathered thereabout, they entered the Klamath River and started upstream at once. Thus do wild things adjust themselves in measure to altered conditions in their endeavor to survive.

By now a change had come over Chinook. Although he and Queen were still silvery-colored and fresh-run from the sea, his nose, or proboscis, was becoming longer, while he was growing a mouthful of terrier-sized teeth. And there was a reason. The teeth were for defense against enemies that might intrude upon his mate and himself during their spawning, while the hooknose was intended to expedite the digging of a redd nest in the sand—a task at which male salmon and steelhead-rainbows appear remiss, since they stand guard while the females do most of the work.

And now began the pilgrimage to the waters of their birth that their species might continue, and themselves keep a rendezvous with death. Both Chinook and Queen had ceased feeding, although occasional spawning adults will take their own roe—a trait that seems more pronounced in recent years as their numbers decrease. Not a few salmon will hit spinners—hence the Klamath fishing rush—but these lures simulate enemies at their spawning beds and arouse their desire to fight or kill, and not to feed.

Ahead of Chinook and Queen were over 150 miles of river—much of it fast water—before they could reach their birthplace in the Little Shasta. To traverse that gauntlet, they would beat themselves into fungus-ridden "sore-tails" ere they fulfilled their destiny. Pride of achievement was denied them. Their role was to procreate and die.

Impossible be it to take issue with the scheme of things, since mankind's small knowledge lacks understanding. But when it is known that steelhead-rainbows undergo the same ordeal or worse, and live to return to the sea comparatively unscathed—or stay in fresh water as they may choose—the salmon's lot seems merciless, an unexplainable discrimination.

The river above tidewater also contained boats and, since these were regarded as enemies regardless of location, Chinook and Queen hid in deep pools during the day and moved upstream by night only.

After a time, when they reached swifter water, most of the boats disappeared. Because of this, Chinook's mate ran into trouble at Blue Creek mouth. They had begun to travel partly by day when a wriggling thing plopped into the water beside her and apparently tried to escape.

Queen had no desire to eat the thing. But it angered her, and she struck it as she would an interloper around the spawning redd.

A fisherman, casting from shore, set his hook—and the battle for life began. Queen was beginning to turn dark— as was her mate—in the forewarnings of death, but she was still charged with vitality from the sea. She turned and raced downstream, with Chinook following.

This fisherman had a lighter outfit than that which had hooked Chinook at sea. Also, its leader was made of plastic. And so, when the female salmon sought refuge under a snag-tangle, that leader broke. But for what remained of her days, Queen was to carry a spinner in her mouth— so deeply was its hook embedded.

Then the first fall storm descended upon Father Klamath's watershed, and the river with its tributaries rose overnight and became muddy; whereupon angling for a time ceased. Protected by rising and roily waters, the pair of salmon worked their way steadily upstream, resting frequently in calmer places en route. Others of their kind were on the same mission, as well as steelhead-rainbows, but they paid them no heed.

Ten days after they left the Pacific, Chinook and Queen reached the confluence of the Klamath and its largest tributary, the Trinity River, within the Hoopa Indian Reservation. Here the Indians had treaty rights to net the rivers— a practice forbidden by law elsewhere. Here again the pair of king-chinooks were fortunate, for the Trinity River had the lesser flow and the Indians were netting from that stream only. And so, while toll was taken from one river, salmon ascending the other went free. Thus did Father Klamath, with his mightier flow, protect his own.

It is nearly a hundred miles from the Klamath-Trinity confluence to the mouth of Shasta River, and the pair of salmon took a month to breast the rough waters before they reached that stream to which their own Little Shasta was tributary. As the main Klamath grew smaller with each mile upstream, fishermen increased, while marauding bears fished the side riffles. Chinook and Queen escaped these hazards and, mortally battered now, started on that last lap, from which there would be no return.

Up the main Shasta River they went, sensing now that the end of their journey was near. When they reached the mouth of the Little Shasta, they paused but briefly in the confluence pool before starting up the smaller stream of their nativity. They were sad shadows of their once-glorious selves—even as had been their progenitors before.

At last, it appeared as if their objective was to be fulfilled. But no . . . A gang of human drifters, feeling secure from the law in this remote area, were staging an orgy of murder. It was simple, when salmon started to ascend the riffles of this shallow stream, to shoot them from shore or spear them as they struggled to pass through. The salmon's flesh was half rotten from sores, fungus, and the oncoming of death; but no matter. It was sport to kill them. Food was not the issue. These worthy citizens were on relief.

Queen got through the pillage—with a gaping spear-slash at the base of her tail, which would cripple her efforts in excavating a redd nest.

Chinook was caught by a shotgun blast when, back

partly exposed, he tried to ascend a riffle. The outlaws did not bother to pick up his shattered remains.

A day later, Queen arrived alone at the vicinity of Chinook's and her birthplaces. The drive of her ancestors still carried on, but death was summoning ever stronger. Feebly, almost half-heartedly, she tried to hollow out a redd—faithful to the last, but no longer able.

And then a minor miracle occurred. A young jack, or grilse salmon, that had escaped the kill downstream because of his speed and smaller size, arrived. At first, his desire was only to eat eggs. Later, when no large male appeared to drive him away, he seemed to sense the exigency and helped the female salmon with her digging.

Together, they observed nature's age-old ritual—Queen laying her eggs with dying effort, and young Jack completing the cycle with his life-giving milt. As compared to a full-grown male, vigor was denied him, but he gave his best. Then when Queen, too far gone to help, had drifted downstream to gasp her last, young Jack obeyed the edict of Manitou. Carefully he covered the redd's new-laid eggs.

That accomplished, he, too, seemed to give up. Perhaps he would live for a few days, but his end was as certain as Queen's.

A night or so later, the season's first snowfall arrived. The drifters, assured of their keep, headed down the highway to a warmer clime. A white-clad peace settled over the forests and hills of the Klamath-Siskiyou domain.

Beneath a riffle in the Little Shasta River, as in uncounted years past, a clutch of king-chinook eggs awaited the call of spring to hatch. Its newborn might not be so sturdy as Chinook's siring would have made them. But they would carry on . . . How far, no man is given to know.

Size Doesn't Always Count

Until timber loggers began invading the age-old Redwood Empire forests, Ivan the black bear had lived an uneventful life.

When the logging railroads were built, together with much noise, the felling of trees and swarming of men, Ivan had been more resentful than afraid. In time, others of his kind began to disappear mysteriously, but Ivan was endowed with better than average acumen for his kind and kept clear of chance-taking situations.

One item about mankind interested him. Their habitations were rife with succulent odors. More and more, Ivan's well-developed sense of smell told him of things to eat that he never had been able to find in the woods. These held promise of gastronomic joy.

However, Ivan was conservative by nature and inclination, and he had seen packs of dogs chase other bears up trees, and heard the ear-jarring bang-bang of guns. On investigation, he had found bears' blood and fur on the ground, which aroused fear.

Cause and effect were beyond Ivan, but the emanations of death were not. And these appeared to come with men, dogs, and shooting. Other animals either feared him or let him alone. But these new foes in his ancestral timberlands seemed to prey upon his kind which, for Ivan, upset law and order. Nor did he know what to do about this visitation.

And so, Ivan became more cautious. After his mate of the previous year disappeared, he turned solitary. It was not that he mourned her especially, since his species does not

forage in pairs. Rather, he avoided all association in this
new and uncertain time.

None the less, those odors from the timber loggers' camps
continued to intrigue him. They hinted at things different
from the mountain beavers he dug out, or the salmon he
caught in the streams during the fall spawning runs. Even
the taste of wild honey from occasional raids on bees'
nests—a delicacy which bears relish—lost part of its appeal.
Ivan wanted something new.

Ivan's food embraced a wide range. In fact, there are
few items on mankind's bill of fare, whether flesh or plant,
that black bears will not eat. Wild berries and many kinds
of roots were staple diet, while an occasional foray into an
apple orchard some miles off his regular beat pleased him.

Too, there were certain young redwood trees whose soft
inner bark contained a vitamin sweet which, at times, he
craved. Nor was he alone in this seeming peculiarity. Many
of his kind reveled in stripping sizeable saplings during
summer's growing period. This, had he but known it, was
the cause of much of the bear killing in his area. In fact,
there were certain sections of Ivan's Sequoia Creek watershed where acres of once-promising young timber had been
devastated—which detracted not a little from the lumber-
men's peace of mind.

In the comparatively mild winter of the northwestern
California coastal forests, black bears tend to hibernate
rather less than their relatives in the snowbound interior
regions. While Ivan went into winter retirement as usual
that season, he emerged from his lair in a remote canyon
during a warm period to catch steelhead-rainbow trout.
These lusty fish ran up to fifteen pounds weight and were
especially to his liking if they contained roe.

Sequoia Creek's water was high and roily from recent
rains, which made fishing difficult. After several chilly dous-
ings, Ivan managed to knock a salmon-sized trout ashore
and enjoy a meal.

During this foray, Ivan had kept his faculties alerted for sounds and smells of mankind. But there seemed to be none. Climbing from the stream bed to higher ground, he made a detailed reconnaissance, but still there seemed no evidence. Nor could he sense men's presence anywhere. Winter had brought a shutdown of their logging operations; a thing beyond his scope to comprehend.

Reassured in measure, Ivan ambled along the logging railroad right-of-way, principally because it offered easier traveling. His every sense was alert and at the slightest sound or smell of danger he would have plunged into the junglelike underbrush. He stopped once or twice to investigate mountain beavers' burrows, but decided the reward was not worth the task of digging them out.

Suddenly a spent whiff of mankind's activities caught his nose. He paused, blinking nearsighted eyes in an effort to see what might be ahead. But the smell warned of no danger—only that human beings had lived there some time before.

A curve of the railroad brought him within proximity of a small camp and commissary, now closed for the winter. He slipped into the brush and watched for several minutes. There was no doubt about the matter. His surveillance assured him the place was uninhabited.

After a time, he made bold to approach the camp buildings and inspect. From one of these came faint but unmistakable odors whose succulence he recalled so well from the past. Apparently the food which interested him was hidden in this man den.

But Ivan was nervous. The unknown held forth here. He investigated the several small bunkhouses and sheds with meticulous care. They smelled neither of food nor recent human occupancy. Finally he returned to the commissary shack. This was where it was. . . .

For some time, he tried various boards and corners of the building. The only place that seemed to yield was a none too heavily constructed back door. It was surrounded by watertight sills and sides, which made it impossible for him to slip a claw into a crack and take hold. However, it moved slightly when he pushed against it.

All this was new to the black bear, and for some time he pondered the situation, at a loss as to how to proceed. By now, his fears had subsided. He was becoming more and more determined to break into this hiding place. Also the door in question was on the shack's lee side, and the tempting odors were stronger there. He pushed against the barrier several times, surprised that it did not yield, since it would move slightly.

Then, in sudden exasperation, Ivan raised on his hind feet and swung a blow onto it with his forepaw. A splintering crash—and his forearm was inside the door beyond the elbow. He jerked it free in alarm, backed away, and for several minutes peered, smelled, and listened.

Now, however, the odor that had interested him fairly billowed out of the hole he had punched. He returned to the raid, seized the door's battered edges—and in moments had ripped out an entrance.

Once inside, and again Ivan was puzzled. No food of any kind was in sight, despite overwhelming evidence via his nose that it was there. Instead, there were peculiar objects piled atop one another like so many rocks—but they were not rocks.

He slipped an exploring paw around one of them and—SNAP!—something seized his foretoes with the suddenness of a rifle shot.

With a hoglike snort, Ivan bolted out of the broken door, taking part of it with him, and fled into the nearby brush.

There he stopped to examine the thing that was clinging to his forepaw and causing it to smart. Now Ivan had not the remotest idea what a rattrap might be, but he did have perception enough to realize that this thing had made a fool of him. He brushed it off with one swipe and crushed it in his jaws. That done, he returned to his job of cache burgling in righteous indignation.

For a few moments, he smelled the stacked cartons and cases. Then, selecting one whose odor was more attractive than the others, he slashed it open with claws that could rip a bull apart.

Several dozen tin cans rattled across the floor. Too intent now to be surprised, Ivan seized one in his jaws and crushed it. A juicy-goo of beef soup rewarded him. It was delicious. This was what he had wanted. He dropped the can onto the floor, licked its sides, and then smacked it with his heavy palm. Soup splattered all about him. He slurped it up joyfully and then flattened several more cans. He had found a treasure more wonderful than anything in a lifetime before.

What Ivan then proceeded to do to that ill-fated cache of canned goods was pitiful—from a man's viewpoint—but sheer delight to him. Canned meats, beans, and fruit, all manner of soups, tamales, sugar, syrups, catsup, canned sardines, salmon, and pungent-tasting anchovies—and heaven knows what-all—were mixed and eaten amid a conglomeration of smashed cartons and cases, flattened tin cans, and broken bottles.

For two days—until a spell of bad weather plus a touch of indigestion drove him back into hibernation—Ivan feasted and glutted in a manner that would have scandalized a Roman. That there might be repercussions was beyond his ken. All Ivan knew was that he had discovered a good thing. And, thanks to a durable constitution, he made the most of it.

A couple of weeks later, when Ivan had slept it off and a spell of pre-spring weather had set in, he again emerged from seclusion and headed for the ravished camp commissary. As he approached, his sense of smell, together with instinctive foreboding, warned him that the situation had changed. Death and danger were in the air.

The man den was still there, but the shattered door had disappeared. A blood-and-metal odor dominated the air, instead of food. And the blood was that of one of his own kind, while the metal was that of traps—a danger against which he had been schooled as a cub.

Ivan had sense enough not to go near the place. His nose and instincts told him all he needed to know without further investigation. The men had returned and trapped a bear at the raided cache.

That another had paid the price for his raiding meant nothing to Ivan. Except to a mother animal with young, life in the wilds is a matter of everyone for himself—more direct, perhaps, than mankind's scheme of things, but basically the same.

As spring approached and his semihibernation ended, Ivan resumed food gathering as usual. He caught more steelhead trout, dug out various rodents' nests, raided bees, and chewed up bulbs and roots. But those tidbits in the man den were not forgotten. Rather, he cruised afar, looking for more such discoveries.

About this time, the logging crews were returning to the woods. With them came freshly stocked commissaries, but always there was a man on guard. True, at night many of them left, but some stayed in the camps. Ivan was thwarted.

When newly laid rails first brought locomotives into Ivan's woods, he had given these behemoths a wide berth. What with their formidable size and their bellowing and running about, he regarded them as living things, mighty beyond his scope. In time, he learned that they stayed on men's trails instead of dashing through the forest after him and, while they were dominant, they were not active enemies.

There were even occasions when he would gape in fascination when one would thunder past with its captive men, while dragging broken trees behind it. He himself feared human beings, and avoided them entirely. But the roaring fire giants feared nothing and seemed to own the men.

Ivan had selected an observation point, concealed among rocks, to which he came frequently as summer arrived. Here he would watch the fire giants, feeling ever more sure of himself.

One morning, one of them suddenly stopped not too far from Ivan's vista point and disgorged men and objects from a man den it had with it. Then, just as suddenly, it picked up its men and roared away. While this was occurring, Ivan had been startled and had shrunk down into his place of concealment.

Later, when the situation had been quiet for some time, he ventured down from his hideout. Those objects left by the fire giant had a familiar appearance. More than that— they smelled faintly of last winter's memorable raid. Nor did they appear suspicious.

Investigation on the spot confirmed Ivan's hopes. With the uninhibited delight of a child turned loose in a candy shop, he slashed and tore into the succulent cargo, squashing cans right and left as he feasted. Nor would he leave the scene until a locomotive whistle up the line gave warning—and then he retreated reluctantly, feeling that the fire giant had left a gift, rather than wanting to do harm.

It was past midday, and Ivan was sleeping in the security of his canyon den, when he was aroused by the oncoming clamor of a dog pack. All too well he knew what that meant.

He slipped out of his den and worked his way farther up a timbered draw until he reached a pass through which the dogs would have to climb, one at a time. Here he concealed himself.

The pack was not long in arriving. As its leader scrambled upward and cleared the narrow opening, a blow from the side killed him instantly. Twice more in quick succession this occurred before the clamor was silenced. Down

in the draw, Ivan could hear the voices of men. He climbed
farther up the mountainside, crossed a ridge, and left
the vicinity of his slayings.

Thus, in a day's events, a killer bear's reputation got its
start. And, through that same day's events, Ivan learned
more about dogs and hunters at first hand. Thereafter, his
cunning and sagacity intensified.

As his store of information expanded, Ivan became increasingly elusive. Twice, as summer wore on, he staged
hit-and-run raids on camp commissaries. That he was becoming ever more unpopular was evidenced by a couple of
flesh grazes from bullets, while another dog pack met par-
tial destruction when it seemed that he had been cornered
at last.

Ivan had sense enough not to overplay his successes,
however, and kept out of sight between forays—to such
extent, in fact, that no one had been able to locate his new
hideout, deep in the timbered hills.

One small, remote logging camp was now under Ivan's
surveillance. Despite the provender he could find in such
abundance in the wilds, he still hankered for the tasty
comestibles that were to be found in mankind's habitations.
He now avoided the larger camps. As a result, when other
bears were killed, they were at times mistaken for the prime
offender—only to have it discovered later that Ivan was still
at large.

This remote camp was operated by one man, as Ivan
soon learned. This man, the camp cook, was systematic.
Almost daily he would leave the camp in the afternoon
and, fly-rod in hand, descend into a canyon alongside to
try his luck; for there were large trout in the stream below.

For some two weeks, off and on, Ivan kept watch on that
camp. He concealed himself in heavy brush around the
clearing, and never came and went over the same route
twice. Also, he had his escape way carefully planned—
together with a killing ambush—in case of dogs.

At last, the time seemed propitious. The cook had left for his afternoon fishing, and all that remained in the camp was a white cat—an ineffective creature beneath a bear's notice. Ivan had planned his campaign well. The loggers were two miles away, the cook was down in the canyon—the time was right for action. He emerged from the nearby clearing and, with head swinging to and fro as he sniffed, listened and strained his nearsighted eyes for a better view, headed for the commissary shack.

But to the best-laid plans of even bears, the unexpected may come. That white cat had a litter of newborn kittens in the cook shanty, and she was devoted to them with that courage beyond courage which man calls mother love.

When Ivan was yet ten feet from the commissary door, he was met by a screaming, spitting fury whose raised-up fur swelled her appearance to half again natural size. Tillie the cat was holding the fort. Then it happened. . . . Straight for Ivan's face with an explosive "FFOW!" came a fighting bundle of fur, armed with hawk-talon claws that raked his eyes.

Ivan tossed his head upward with a startled grunt, and swung one forepaw at the mother cat as a man would slap at a troublesome insect. But the upfling of the bear's head had dislodged Tillie's hold. She flew into the air above him, missing a murderous slash by an inch.

Tillie had to land atop Ivan's back. There was no alternative. And that she did—with claws and teeth raking through his summer-thinned fur. To Ivan, the pain involved was nothing, but the element of surprise was complete. Nothing like this had ever happened to him before.

No longer was the black bear sure of himself. This was beyond comprehension—and might bring men to the scene. More than that—five pounds of cat was morally in the right, and three hundred pounds of bear knew it. Straight for the brush he headed, with hind feet all but scratching his ears with every stride—while a screaming, battling handful of fury spurred him on as no jockey ever rode a horse.

About that time the cook, who had wanted to pick up more fishing gear, arrived shouting—but was outdistanced with never a chance. Into the brush plunged Ivan like a big, scared pig, with Tillie digging clawfuls of hair through to blood by now. How far she might have ridden to undying fame must remain in doubt, for a low-hanging branch whisked her off like a bit of fluff. Unharmed, she hurried back to her babies, still muttering of battle.

. . . To this day, old-timers in the Sequoia Creek area will recount with emotion the story of intrepid Tillie. And woe unto him who professes disbelief. Tillie belongs with the immortals.

As for Ivan, he wanted no part of that camp. For some time thereafter, he forsook the haunts of mankind and sulked in solitary dudgeon. What men, guns, dogs, and even locomotives had failed to do, one little mother cat that feared no living thing had accomplished.

The end came toward the close of the following winter. As before, Ivan had awakened from his light hibernation during a warm period, and had ventured out after food. This time, he did not go after steelhead trout or other prey, but headed for a camp commissary that had been boarded up. His coming, however, had been anticipated, and there is no doubt that the bear found in a cleverly concealed trap was the original and only Ivan, for no bear like him was ever encountered again.

Wings from the North

Harfang, the great arctic snow owl, was starving. A winter of grim foreboding had descended upon the tundras of Keewatin, where the life-tide rose and ebbed with the sun in northern Canada. Instinct had warned Harfang that this would not be like any other winter he had known before. Always, during his seven years of life in polar latitudes, there had been food in the darkness and snow. This time there was almost none, and the icy hush of famine hung over his world, while a retreating sun glowed ever more briefly to the south, and blacked out.

Something had been wrong with the life-giving light all year. Grasses, lichens, and mosses seemed to lack substance and vitality. The sun had shone brightly enough during the polar summer, but some factor in its rays was deficient. Something essential to normal growth was blocked off, and the little creeping creatures upon the neo-glacial tundras had withered as from a plague.

Hardest hit were the lemmings, those gopherlike rodents of the Arctic, noted for their suicide migrations. These had begun to disappear in midsummer, and their young were few and poor. So, in measure, the snow owls had suffered, since they preyed upon the lemmings for food. All life had suffered, since its survival depended upon the sun's largess.

Migrant birds had left long before, prompted by instinct to go south sooner than in normal years, while the snow-shoe rabbits and ptarmigan seemed to have disappeared. Deep beneath the snow and ice, a few muskrats huddled in their nests and subsisted upon what food they had been able to store. Even the ermines and little arctic foxes, which could be prey to an owl desperate with hunger, were mysteriously missing. Nature's continuity had been broken, and death was upon the tundras.

Like a specter in the silence of starlight and aurora, the big, white-mantled owl winnowed back and forth in search of any living thing that might furnish fuel for his body. Blue-chilled stars flared from a black sky, and at times there was not enough vapor in the sub-zero atmosphere to make them twinkle. In the void of interstellar space, so near to earth's surface, the northern lights flamed, flickered, and flamed again.

After a time, Harfang alighted upon a hummock where he and Nyctea, his mate, had nested in the spring. His rounded head appeared as large as that of a year-old child, while his length neared thirty inches of purest white— making him one of the most beautiful of birds.

His wings, which were swift enough to fly down a wild duck in the air, spread five and a half feet from tip to tip. His body was so thickly clad with furlike plumage that despite its gaunt condition and the fifty-below-zero cold, the life that pulsed within stayed fever-warm.

Harfang's eyes were perhaps his most impressive feature, since they looked forward like those of a man, instead of sidewise as with most birds. Also, they were designed to see equally well under the never setting sun of Keewatin's summer or in the endless dark that offset it. Their almost oriental slant gave the owl an appearance of mystic wisdom which he did not feel. All he knew was that his life fire must have fuel or, before long, its warmth would sink and his being would be snuffed out.

Another tribulation was upon Harfang—Nyctea had disappeared two days before. Harfang had returned many times to their nest-hummock, and once, when he caught a stray gull, he had hurried there to share it with her. His tension was becoming acute now. Inside his head, a surer instrument than any made by mankind was warning him that a great storm was on the way, and that he must leave at once or perish. But he would not leave without Nyctea, for the snow owl mates but once, and that for a lifetime.

Suddenly the big owl tensed. Not even his hearing, which could detect a rat's squeal a quarter mile away, had caught it; but a finer vibration within him told him something was approaching. He turned and peered into the blue-black dark which, to his eyes, was like a steel engraving that showed every detail. Before long, he saw his oncoming mate.

Down from the boreal sky Nyctea came—a great frosty bird on wings as silent as thought. She skimmed over the snow for seventy yards, veered upward, and alighted beside Harfang like a wraith.

But the pair of snow owls made no demonstration. Harfang had not flown to meet her, nor would he accord her so much as a glance now—whereupon Nyctea uttered a hawk-like "cree-ee," one of the snow owl's few notes. Harfang ruffled himself and stared across the tundra. His mate did not need to tell him that she had found no hunting. For a time, the two ghostly figures stood statuelike atop their hummock. Then, as one bird, they took to the air. Upward into the night they soared, with long, even wing beats, ascending toward the aurora and the stars. And their course lay to the southwest, toward the far-off Pacific coast, away from the Great Storm to come.

Hour upon hour they flew, mounting once above a disturbance to avoid winds that would tax their weakened wings—two ghostly bits of life, pulsing through space and cold, thousands of feet above the earth. Always they bore south, with a veering toward the west, while the storm of a decade loomed against the horizon behind them. Never had they made a flight of such magnitude before, but the Messenger of Manitou, whose care it is to watch over all wild things, was pointing the way.

Toward the end of their second day aloft, both owls began to falter. Their bodies had been emaciated when they left Keewatin. Now the strain of continuous flying was reducing them to feather-wrapped skeletons. When a southerly gale began tossing them about like derelicts in a typhoon, they were forced downward. There is a point beyond which even the fittest cannot carry on.

Heavy snow clouds were riding the wind by now, and beneath these clouds they found themselves over a wooded and rolling countryside quite unlike their native tundras. A man came into sight in the waning day. Both Harfang and Nyctea knew what he was at once, because men had robbed their nest and shot at them two years before.

The next thing both owls saw, as they descended toward a group of farm buildings, was a bird that resembled a ptarmigan. Here was food, and they swooped upon it.

The farmer stepped outside just as a pair of fiery-eyed phantoms dropped out of a snow flurry and enveloped one of his hens. The sight froze him, open-mouthed.

Harfang seized the prey, but his tired wings did not have the strength to lift it from the ground. For a long second he beat in frost-winged silence until Nyctea, sensing danger, came to his aid. Together they whisked the squawking chicken into the air, while the man shouted and ran back into his barn.

Moments later, blasts of that noise the owls associated with nest robbery smote their ears, but Harfang and Nyctea were safely under way, screened by snowfall and murky light. They flew with their burden until exhaustion forced them to land. And then they ate. Never did renewed strength circulate through their bodies with more welcome warmth. Had Nyctea not helped, Harfang's wings would have joined the farmer's trophies in the barn.

And now, although these visitors from the arctic silence did not know it, they were entering the domain of a new enemy—man the maker of noise. Famine, the foe that had driven them out of Keewatin, was left behind. But in its place, increasing as they few southward, was noise—an enemy that never seemed to rest.

By now, the Great Storm was spreading from Saskatchewan into the United States, and the pair of owls rode the vanguard of it, veering southwest like flotsam ahead of an onrushing tide. In two days they had crossed the Continental Divide through Montana and Idaho and were into eastern Oregon, still battling the elements in a blizzard that shattered records and paralyzed railroads.

They soon learned that food was more abundant around the habitations of mankind. They also learned that human beings were less apt to be about in the comparative quiet of night and, when they were, they seemed strangely blind. So Harfang and Nyctea hunted only by night and survived, while others of their tribe succumbed to guns during the day. Their relatives, the native owls, knew the rules from generations of experience. But most of the arctic visitors knew men only from rare glimpses, and were as naïve in this more populous and noisy land as Eskimos in the city.

Still the Great Storm continued, howling across the northwest, while Harfang and Nyctea retreated ever farther southward until they came to the Klamath River mouth. Had they lingered another day in Keewatin, they could not have fought their way out alive. Now, however, instinct called a halt in this land at the storm's edge. They had gone far enough.

To these newcomers from the arctic barrens, the Redwood Empire shore seemed like a land of new-found spring. Its warmth troubled them at first—although mankind went about bundled up and complaining of an unusual winter. A light snow patched the ground. Food was so plentiful that they no longer needed to hunt around mankind's places of abode, and there were days when Harfang and Nyctea ate almost their own weight in waterfowl. This, together with respite for the Great Storm, soon put them in prime condition. But the baneful element was noise. Noise was everywhere, beating upon their sensitive ears, and already a home-desire was upon the owls. With the first harbinger of winter's end, they would start their northward hegira, away from the clamor and confusion.

One afternoon, when Harfang was in a tree beside a tributary creek, he saw a large fish with its dorsal fin out of water, working its way up a shallow riffle. He dove upon it at once, sinking his fur-clad talons deep into its back.

But the fish was a fifteen-pound steelhead-rainbow trout —nearly three times Harfang's weight—and strong with the urge of its spawning run. It bucked and thrashed like a bull trying to unseat a rider, while Harfang hung on, beating his wings in futility. Whereupon the huge trout turned and raced downstream into a snag-hole. In an instant, Harfang was under water, with his wings twisting behind him, as he all but strangled and strove to let go.

Down into deep water they surged and under a log jam, where Harfang's wings were caught in debris. Water seemed to crush into his lungs, and he knew fear as never before, while his legs were all but pulled out of joint in an agony of stretching.

Then his talons straightened, and the powerful trout tore free. A reaction that was half instinctive, half convulsive, pushed him out of the deathtrap, and he fought to the surface where Nyctea was hovering in anxiety. She helped him flop ashore, where he lay half drowned.

After that, the pair of snow owls fished together. They would perch on rocks beside riffles until a steelhead-rainbow of acceptable size came by. If the fish was too large for one partner, the other came to the rescue, as in the case of their first chicken. Even so, they took an occasional ducking—but they caught fish.

Nearly a month passed, and as the January moon went into its wane the dusky horned owls of the redwoods turned their attention to nesting. A pair of these ferocious birds

considered themselves sole owners of a redwood glen that
Harfang and Nyctea had chosen for a daytime hideout
and looked upon the snow owls as invaders to be killed.
Although these natives were somewhat smaller than their
artic relatives, they were fighters that could whip eagles
and feared nothing except mankind's guns.

Late one afternoon the horned owls began hooting deep
in a somber copse. By sundown they had worked themselves into a fury. Darkness was rising from the forest floor,
and Harfang and Nyctea were about to leave—when they
suddenly found themselves fighting for their lives. Nor were
their longer wings any help, since their short-winged attackers could dodge in and about the trees with ease.
Twice Harfang had clutches of feathers torn out, and once
he was almost borne to the ground when his foe got a
chance hold. Even Nyctea, who grappled with the female
horned owl, was being driven from his side.

The snowl owl is no coward in battle. Had the situation
been reversed, Harfang and Nyctea would have fought to
the death. As it was, they knew they did not belong in this
place, and so they wanted only to escape these dark-
winged terrors that cracked their beaks like mad things
and lusted to kill. Upward and clear of the towering trees,
the battle raged. Ermine-down feathers swirled like snow-
flakes as the arctic owls took to the open air, where their
superior speed saved them. After a quarter-mile chase, the
horned owls turned back, triumphant.

Next morning, Harfang and Nyctea sought shelter in another grove, near which was camped a trailer colony. As
day brightened, automobiles rattled back and forth, children shrilled, dogs yapped, men shouted, radios squawked,
and the two snow owls, high in a redwood tree, were kept
awake and on edge by the din.

By midmorning, Harfang and Nyctea decided to leave.
They did not fly high, as they had done when the horned

owls attacked them, but dropped low among the trees and headed up a ravine.

Two men were skulking in the brush, on hunt for anything that might fill their stewpots at the camp. When they saw the great white-winged birds approaching, they stood for a moment transfixed. Then one of them jerked a shotgun to his shoulder.

The motion caught Harfang's eye too late. Deafening blasts smote his ears, and he was knocked off course by a blow. Nyctea cried out and fell—nor was there anything Harfang could do. He fled with every ounce of his wounded strength.

The men looked at Nyctea's almost human head, with her mysterious eyes already filming in death, and swore. One of them kicked the quivering victim, and rapier-sharp talons pierced his shoe. The man yelped and jerked free. He pointed his gun and blasted a gaping hole through Nyctea's body, scattering blood-sprayed down among the ferns.

Harfang's plumage had deflected much of the scattered shot and, while he was shocked and bleeding, he was not fatally wounded. He continued up the ravine and alighted in a fir thicket atop a ridge. The intuition of wild things told him Nyctea was dead.

It was after dark before Harfang dared return to the murder scene, and there he saw. How he might have felt as he stood vigil over what was left of his life partner, is denied superior beings to know. Late that night, Harfang went his way. His wounded muscles had stiffened, and so he did not fly far but hid in the hills, away from sight and sound of man.

For several days, Harfang ventured only far enough from his refuge to catch food. Then, with returning vitality, came a half-felt restlessness. The time had not come for him to go north, for ice-winged tempests still rode the skies of

Keewatin; but he wanted increasingly to be on the move, and needed only a stimulus to start him.

This came abruptly one sundown when an airplane, looking for a lost man, roared so low over Harfang's hideout that it all but brushed the treetops. He fled, but once under way he felt lost and alone. The call to return had not come, nor would he ever again have a mate. And so he drifted into Wyoming, where he ran into a mid-February blizzard.

Harfang paid no attention to the weather, but hunting was poor. On the second night of the storm, he found a large barn with its lower door open and flew into it in search of prey. He did not take time to reconnoiter, as would a native owl. What he wanted was there, and he circled over a hayloft where squeaking and rustling told him of mice.

Scarcely had he begun to hunt, when a tractor approached the door. Harfang flew to the rafters, but even the pigeonholes were closed. The doorway below seemed his only escape, and now that was blocked by the lights of the entering machine. He flew to the highest corner under the roof and hid.

Two men were with the tractor. They clattered and talked for a time. Then the light lights went out, and the barn door rumbled shut with a clang. All was quiet once more, but Harfang had had enough. He circled overhead, watching the tractor, now so silent—and saw the entrance had disappeared! At once he took alarm and began to race back and forth the length of his prison, seeking any way of escape into the protecting night. But the barn was tightly constructed and weatherproof. Not even a swallow could have got out. Harfang was trapped.

When the first light of dawn filtered through a row of small windows, he hurled himself against them, but found them as resistant as the ice they resembled.

Then the door below began to rattle. Harfang flew into his high roof corner to watch. The door opened slightly and stopped. Harfang's heart was drumming. To his fear of confinement was added the fear of the unknown. Abandoning caution, he dived downward at that opening—just as a man started to enter. The surprise was mutual. Harfang banked sharply, and one white-down wing cuffed the man's face. He yelled, dodged out, and slammed the door shut.

Up in his corner again, Harfang heard a babble of voices outside—and then the entire barn lighted up as bright as day. Startled, he took to his wings as the entrance opened and several faces peered up.

To the men below, Harfang's snow-winged flight looked unearthly. "No wonder he scared you," said one of them. "It's a big snowy owl. Hey—don't shoot him! You'll blast a hole through the roof. How did he get in, I wonder?"

"I dunno," said the man who had been frightened. "Why don't you let me build a big cage, and we'll keep him. An' for heaven's sake, make 'em keep that door closed!"

For the rest of the morning, Harfang circled the upper reaches of the barn, while one man hammered intermittently, and others arrived to stare at the splendid captive, and add to the confusion of sound. The noise was intolerable, and several times the broad-winged owl banged against the windows with such force that the men finally fastened hogwire across them for protection.

Toward midday, several men strung a fishnet between long poles and began chasing Harfang back and forth. He was almost caught by this snare at first and thereafter bypassed it in the roof heights. But he was wearing down from tension and fright, and it was only a matter of time until he would be taken.

"All right you fellows, let's eat," announced the ranch owner. "After lunch we'll rig a couple more nets onto a frame, get those high ladders from outside, and gang up on him."

They filed out the door, glancing over their shoulders, and for the moment Harfang was alone. He retreated, panting, to his roof-peak corner. The barn's warmth was adding to his misery.

The storm had lessened during midday, and now a pair of small boys wanted to look at the snowy owl again. They had been inside the barn most of the morning, but the thrill of adventuring alone—especially when their elders forbade—was too tempting.

They tugged at the heavy roller door, secure in the knowledge that they could not be seen from the house, but it stuck. They heaved against it with all their strength—and it rolled halfway open.

Their father had shut off the barn lights over lunchtime to save diesel fuel—and so no reassuring light greeted the boys. They fell back from the opening in fear. It was one thing to watch a ghost-headed will-o'-the-wisp in the light, but quite another when its whereabouts were unknown.

For an instant, Harfang poised in his corner. Then, like a ski-rider plunging down a slope, he flung himself from the roof peak and shot out through the doorway. A dozen wingbeats took him upward and off, leaving the shrill wails of the boys in his wake. He wanted only one thing now—to leave this land and return to Keewatin.

Harfang was nearing Canada when the first harbinger of change-to-come reached him. The storms were not done, but the death hold of winter was loosening. Already a few small birds were about. It was time to go.

Away into the frost mists, straight toward Keewatin, winged Harfang—first of the snow owls to return. Ahead was loneliness while others went about their nesting. But the noise-enemy would no longer menace him in the arctic silence he trusted and understood.

Cradled on the Sea

Dawn laced through the summer sea mists around Patrick's
Point on the Redwood Empire coast. Easy-moving swells
that had crossed leagues of ocean undulated through the
kelp beds close to land—to expire upon the beaches and
against rocks with a quiet sigh. As the mists cleared, hills
garlanded with redwood timber loomed above the shore
line like verdant sentinels ordained by the Creator to keep
watch over the deep. And over the realm there whispered a
peace as ageless as infinity.

In a kelp-grown cove half encircled by a rocky headland,
Nerea the sea otter floated on her back, cradling her first-
born kit, or pup, against her breast. A beautiful and gentle
child of the sea she was—a fur-clad mermaid nearly five
feet in length, vibrant with love for her youngster and the
joy of being alive.

Fortunately, it was not given to Nerea's awareness to
know that the finely-glossed, brownish-black fur whose
thickness protected her from the sea had all but caused
extermination of her species, so ruthlessly had mankind
sought these pelts from the Aleutian Islands to Lower
California over a century before. Belated intervention by
national governments had stayed the clubs, guns, and har-
poons, but for a time it seemed that protection had come
too late. Only a few scattered individuals, now so mis-
trustful that they have ceased to set foot on shore except
during extreme weather, have managed to carry through.

Nerea crooned softly to the warm, new life that suckled
at her dugs, and felt relaxed and serene in this haven amid

her own kind. The herd was small, but her instincts had forgotten that once their number was legion. Her world was the immediate present, and just now she was hungry. However, there was no hurry. First came the needs of her kit.

After a time, the youngster's nursing subsided, while the benign roll of the sea lulled him to sleep. Carefully, Nerea snuggled him into a kelp-cradle, where he floated on his back, head out of water. No human mother could have arranged her baby's bassinet with more loving care.

Satisfied at last, she slipped beneath the surface with a graceful sweep, propelled by webbed hind feet. Down into several fathoms of water she swam, guided by a foot-long tail, to where sea urchins were to be found. In two or three minutes she returned, carrying a couple of these purple relatives of the starfish.

First, she inspected Kit, who was slumbering in peace, unaware of the primary source of his sustenance. Reassured, Nerea rolled over on her back again. There she proceeded to bite holes into the urchins' shells or tests and scoop out their succulent interiors with her tongue.

Breakfast finished, she allowed herself the luxury of a series of roll overs in the brightening sunlight. She inspected Kit again, and straightened an imaginary kink in his cradle.

The sea urchins, while good, had whetted Nerea's appetite for other food. She looked across the kelp at her nearest neighbor and, noting that all seemed well, submerged again—this time in quest of abalones, which took her farther away.

She had gone a fair distance when a vibration in the water grated upon her ears. She surfaced at once. There, ploughing alongside the cove's kelp bed, was a boat—a thing against which memory-instincts inherited from generations of persecuted ancestors cried aloud.

With the swiftness of a startled trout, Nerea submerged, and in a half minute brought up beside the still slumbering

Kit. True, she had seen boats before. On those occasions, however, she had had only herself to consider, and avoiding them was an easy matter.

Now, with progeny more precious than life itself to protect, she stood guard, quivering with anger and fear. She would not take Kit under water except as a last resort—although he had been conceived and born on the sea's bosom. Nor could he swim as yet, since young sea otters, like young seals, must be taught that accomplishment. And Kit, although born with open eyes and the ability to move about, needed at least a week to become mobile in the water—and he was a scant day old.

The boat, however, was not an enemy. It was manned by fisheries researchers who noted the sea otters within the cove with interested eyes, and put away from the area lest the herd be unduly disturbed.

To Nerea, though, boats appeared fully as menacing as killer whales or large sharks—foes of her tribe from time immemorial. Long after the craft had gone away, she stayed by Kit's cradle, abalones forgotten.

Before the sun was high, Kit had been given his first swimming lesson, wherein he showed promise. Finally, with her world at seeming peace again, Nerea nursed him and bedded him down once more. Again she set out after an abalon dinner for herself.

Now an abalone is a sizeable shellfish that clings to rocks with such a grip that men have to pry them loose with tire irons. But the sea otter has a better system than mankind as a rule—although broken abalone shells washed ashore at times give mute testimony to the use of force. Nerea, along with others of her kind, long ago had learned to cruise under water like a shadow, watching for abalones on the move. When these shellfish are shifting base in quest of new pastures, they are vulnerable, since they cannot get a firm hold in time to resist attack.

Thus Nerea, in her quest, spotted an abalone moving

along the ocean bottom. One scoop, and it was hers. Picking up a round rock, she brought it and her prey to the surface alongside Kit's cradle.

And there—after a quick checkup of her youngster—she proceeded to enjoy a feast. She made no attempt to break the abalone's single-sided shell, but rolled over on her back and placed the shellfish on her chest, fleshy side up. Then, using the rock as a hammer, she pounded the squirming flesh into softness.

Again and again she poked her blunt muzzle into the beaten up meat and bit off chunks with her strong, sharp teeth. Within minutes, her repast was finished, and Nerea dropped stone and empty shell overboard.

Satiated now, she scratched off a couple of ectoparasites that had attached themselves to her, folded her arms across her midriff, and, floating on her back, went to sleep. After a time the sun shone on her face, whereupon she placed forepaws across her eyes and slept on, even as Kit . . . cradled on the sea.

But that same sea which was nursery, boudoir, sustenance, and enjoyment of life for Nerea also harbored fearsome enemies. Among the worst of these was Orca the killer whale—that dorsal-finned murderer and outlaw whose terrible jaws could kill sea lions with a single crunch and who, in packs, could tear apart the largest of whales. Even mankind, for all his weapons, shunned Orca, for he is known to have attacked boats.

A month passed, and Kit had become an adept swimmer, now able to dive with Nerea and hold his breath for fair intervals. He was his gentle mother's pride and joy. Never had there been such a cub. At every opportunity she took him calling on friends and neighbors; nor did any of the kindly disposed creatures resent his presence. A new mother with her firstborn was especially welcome, for in some manner beyond definition, the group seemed to feel that its limited entity needed the bolstering up of every new arrival. Its community spirit was as one.

Nerea and Kit had become especially friendly with Nerid, another young female sea otter with her own first-born. Nights, the mothers slept alongside each other, floating upon their backs with babies on their breasts, the while securely tethered to kelp strands to prevent their drifting outside the cove where enemies might threaten.

Several times a day, the two mothers nursed their progeny side by side, while watching other herd members disported themselves amid the kelp pursuing their amours, since their tribe—like human beings—will go courting at any time of the year. Nor are they—perhaps like some human beings again—committed to the creed of monogamy.

Theirs might have appeared an idyllic life in truth, for nature seemingly had favored them, despite occasional buffetings from winter seas or the menace of enemies from the deep. Against such tribulations the kelp beds were their salvation always, for there the raging waters were tempered in measure and marauders on the hunt were thwarted. But against mankind, with its weapons and cunning, the best of their kelp beds and shelter availed them little.

It was at the start of fall when a group of young men, armed with rifles and bottles, made their way through the redwood forests above the sheltered cove and emerged atop the headland overlooking the sea otters' kelp beds.

Great was their surprise to see a number of seal-like animals at rest on their backs in the water below or cavorting through the kelp. Action followed immediately. Bullets pinged around the sea otters' heads. Fortunately, alcohol had dulled the intruders' aim. Most of the frightened herd, demoralized still further by the guns' noise, dove under water and headed toward the outer-sea edge of their kelp bed. Among these were Nerea, Kit, and their two neighbor friends. They were all the more upset when an otter on the surface was hit by a bullet and, crying piteously, rolled over and over, apparently unable to submerge.

In deeper water, beyond the edge of their kelp-haven, the herd bunched together in common distress. So well had they been protected from land attack until now, that their awareness of danger from that source had dimmed. But deep in their beings, instinct shrilled alarm.

It was then that Orca the killer whale, with his grisly squad, came upon them. These murderers were all too familiar to the sea otters. But double adversity had struck so quickly that their faculties were momentarily confused. Before the herd could scatter back among the kelp, several had fallen victim.

Among the first was Nerea, who had rushed to the fore to drive the foes away from Kit, true to mother love to the end. And her life was extinguished in one crunch of jaws beyond her power to circumvent.

Kit was too frightened and confused for purposeful flight, but after a time he groped his way back to the area of his too-few days of babyhood. That his mother was not with him was beyond his comprehension, since she was life itself. After a time, he raised his head above the kelp to look and began crying with the thin wail of a newborn baby. A bullet or two flew by his head, but daylight was waning, and the vandals were tiring of their sport.

All that night, as well as the day and night that followed, Kit clung to the vicinity of his onetime refuge of love and shelter, unable to understand what had happened. His wailing became thinner as hunger took its toll. The cradle rocking of the sea was no benefit, for he was unable to sleep for more than minutes at a time. Nor could he know that the first prewinter storms soon would wrack his kelp-haven. He only knew that he was becoming ever more hungry, cold, and weak—while his mother, source of all warmth, food, and goodness was gone. In time, his senses began numbing in preparation for death.

It was then that a miracle occurred—a phenomenon that materialists might toss aside as mere animal need, not to be confused with perception. Nerid, the female sea otter with whom Nerea had played and hunted, and alongside of whom she had nursed Kit, had lost her own youngster in the confusion that followed the double attack. How it happened, only the gods of the sea might know. Perhaps a marauding shark had followed the killer whales. At all events, Nerid was now without her young. And her heart was heavy with grief.

For two nights and a day, Nerid had searched throughout the span of the kelp bed, calling and crying for her missing pup. Finally, with milk all but bursting from her dugs, she had come back to Nerea's and her former location. True, she had heard Kit's wailing from time to time. But since these were not the sounds of her own young, she had paid them scant heed.

Now mother craving was dominant. Nerid's cub was missing—gone, so far as she could ascertain. Here, on the other hand, was a baby with whom she was already acquainted. He was not her own, but he was in need. Such is the gentleness and compassion of her kind that she took him to her without reserve, and a near-dying Kit nourished himself at the fount of life; nor questioned its authenticity. He snuggled ever deeper against Nerid's dugs, knowing only that what he wanted was there. Together, they cradled on the ebb and flow of the tides, Kit in Nerid's arms— foster mother and son, assured by each other's nearness.

Once adjusted, Kit and his foster mother settled down to life in accord with the tenor of their tribe. Although young sea otters are known to nurse for many months, Kit's education in catching and eating solid foods was well under way ere the first heavy weather hit the redwood coast. Small crabs fascinated him. These gave him his first experience at hunting, and he would eat them while cradled on his new mother's breast. When Nerid went farther

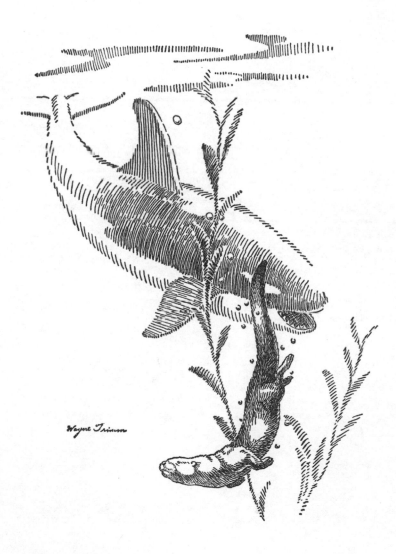

Wayne Trimm

after mussels, scallops, limpets, and clams, he stayed amid the surface kelp, awaiting her return.

He would meet her, all eagerness, when she brought back these delicacies, and watch wide-eyed while she broke them apart. This, Nerid accomplished while floating upon her back and using a rock placed atop her belly as an "anvil." Holding a shellfish in both her forepaws, she would bring it down onto the rock with a smart whack—an act which classifies sea otters as one of the few wild creatures that have learned to use tools.

Once the prey was cracked open, Kit would shove a quivering nose into the delectable flesh, while his provider watched in fond accord. Before long, Kit was bringing up little stones on which he banged equally small crabs with imitative gusto. Thus he grew and learned.

Then one morning the sun rose angry-red in back of the redwood forests, and soon was swallowed by a black curtain. Gone was the peace that belonged in the cove. Wind was blasting, and all nature seemed tense. The sea otters hunted little and gathered in close-pack formation.

A headland to the north protected the otters' cove from northern and prevailing westerly winds—which made that location so desirable. Now, however, a gale was building from the south, and their haven was exposed to direct battering from rising seas.

The kelp beds heaved and twisted. Clusters and strands were torn loose and flung onto beach and rocks where they were pounded into shreds by crashing breakers. To Kit, this was beyond comprehension. Peace and protection had disappeared, and he and Nerid seemed adrift in a world gone mad. A driving rain seared across the water, but he was scarcely aware of that.

For most of that day the herd stayed together, while its members occasionally sought food in the calmer depths. But it was impossible to dine in the usual manner, and they fed sparingly on crabs and sea urchins while tossed about like flotsam.

When what remained of daylight began to dim, the storm worsened. Members of the herd began seeking shelter ashore amid the rocks to get away from encroaching whitecaps which now raced across the kelp beds despite the calming effect of that comparatively dense seaweed.

Nerid knew better than to risk a landing amid the combers that foamed and burst over the rocks. Rather, she led Kit through heavy surf onto a small beach in the cove, and headed for a rock shelter above the sea's reach.

In water, sea otters are graceful creatures that swim with the ease of porpoises and seals. Ashore, they are as awkward as human beings trying to run on all fours, since their shortened forearms have lost their ability to function efficiently as feet. To Kit, this was a new and unpleasant mode of travel—one about which he knew nothing. Somehow he stumbled and wallowed after his guardian and in time, found refuge with her in a clammy crevice slightly elevated above the sea's wrath. There they waited it out together.

The following morning saw the situation changed rather for the worse. A maddened ocean writhed and tore against the redwood coast, its waters one mass of whitecaps and rollers whipped by full gale winds.

Nerid had been watching the situation with knowing eyes. This had happened to her before. Now hunger was making itself felt. And so, when daylight of sorts came, she gave Kit a warning nudge which, interpreted, meant "stay here," and plunged into a receding comber. She disappeared into the roil like a dropped stone.

Kit was disturbed but obedient. He retreated farther into the crevice and huddled in its precarious shelter like a beleaguered puppy. Nerid would return. Instinct assured him of that.

Now the northern Redwood Empire is primarily a pleas-

ant and lovely land. But like any other place on earth, it
can have not only bad weather but also a few unpleasant
and unlovely inhabitants. This particular day, during the
storm's crest, a large octopus, upset by the general disturbance, was on the prowl. Bursting breakers meant little
to him, since he could cling to rocks with death-grip
tentacles and let the water surge about him. Also, these
same vacuum-cupped extremities were sure disaster to anything that ran afoul of their clutch. True, his kind are not
numerous, but they exist—as skin divers can testify.

An unusually high wave lifted the hideous apparition almost into Kit's crevice. Receding water left him in front of
the little sea otter, whence each surveyed the other—but
with differing reactions.

Octo was the first to act. He sent out an exploratory
tentacle, more in curiosity than desire. Kit shrank back even
farther. Then, when the unknown thing half encircled him
in a clammy crawl, he bit it in instinctive self-defense.
Instantly the eel-like threat jerked away.

But now Octo was angry. He grated his bonelike jaws,
which were designed to crush and poison prey seized by
his tentacles. He advanced slightly and threw out several
tentacles as one unit. With never a chance to defend himself, Kit was enmeshed like a fly in a spider's web. He was
desperate, but struggle and cry though he might, he had no
recourse against this foe.

In his dim way, Octo the bloodsucker was gratified.
Never had he made such a catch. He backed down the
rocks, pulling his enmeshed prey, and let an incoming
comber surge over them. He was unable to swim in his
usual reverse manner, which made progress slow, but he
was able to hang on as he descended into deeper water.
Kit was doomed.

Nerid was returning with a couple of protesting crabs,
swimming well beneath the storm-wracked surface, when
a disturbance amid nearby rocks caught her attention.

More because of curiosity than anything else, she swerved off course to investigate. And there, in the dim murk, she found her adopted progeny squirming in the monster's grip.

The crab captives, suddenly freed, scuttled away—while Nerid rushed to the attack. This was something beyond her experience, but mother love took command. Like an avenging fury, she drove straight for the octopus' ghastly head, where poisonous crusher met slashing teeth. Gentle though the sea otter is, Kit's peril pulsed adrenalin into Nerid's blood stream to cope with the dire emergency.

Octo had no adrenalin in his fish-cold blood. While he fought with beak and tentacle, he soon was sorely wounded from the knifelike teeth of his attacker. Now he wanted only to get away. He let go of Kit, squirted quantities of inky fluid into the water, and retreated.

That was enough. Groping in the blackened water about her, Nerid found a now unconscious Kit and bore him to the surface with desperate speed. There, braving seas that burst high into the air, she managed somehow to drag him onto the rocks and reach the comparative dryness of their crevice refuge. But Kit lay motionless and limp.

Nerid was not versed in the science of first aid to the drowning. She cried as any bereft human mother might have done and turned the inert Kit over and around, time and again. Perhaps this accomplished the desired end. Only Manitou, who watches over all wild things, could know. Kit began to gasp, then retched and coughed out a spray of water, while Nerid hovered over him in quivering devotion. In a few minutes, he opened his eyes and looked at her, at first in fear. Then as awareness returned and his breathing became easier, he snuggled against her like a frightened child, while Nerid crooned assurance and licked him with her tongue.

Finally the Storm King's wrath was assuaged. Almost apologetically, the once angry clouds stole away and the gale subsided. A late fall sun again smiled upon land and sea, while Indian summer returned for a farewell blessing.

Again, Nerid and Kit frolicked among the kelp beds with their kin, hunting for sea urchins, shellfish, and crabs. That experience with Octo and the storm had changed Kit from a baby to a sturdy youngster. Already, he was beginning to use stones as tools, and never again would he be bewildered by heavy weather. He was ready. . . .

A setting sun had turned the ocean's blue to gold. That peace which seems especially to bless the Redwood Empire as the year wanes, lay over land and sea. In the gently undulating swells amid the kelp beds, Nerid and Kit made ready for the night. He was a young tribe member now, and no longer would sleep in his foster mother's arms. Rather, he tended to look protectively about ere they settled for the night. And Nerid was pleased that her male child was becoming aware of his responsibilities.

Wolves of the Deep

A sullen Pacific Ocean surged against the shores of Trinidad Head. Gray skies partly obscured the hills and redwood forests. All nature seemed restless and ill at ease. Even the sea birds appeared to have sought surcease ashore, for almost none were sitting upon the water. Along the coast, a series of rocky reefs loomed above the sea, less than a half mile from shore. Here numbers of sea lions had drawn themselves well above the water line and lay so quietly that they resembled rocks.

The sea lions were apprehensive. And, despite their formidable size, they had reason to share the feeling of foreboding that brooded over the scene. For Orca the killer whale was in the area—that grim timber wolf of the deep which hunts in packs and against whom the mightiest denizens of the sea have no defense. Even the commercial fishing fleets view his presence with unease and avoid his path; for Orca will destroy nets and has an uncertain temper.

Like a scimitar of death, a dorsal fin nearly six feet in height rose from the water. Beneath it was a thirty-foot body whose blackness accentuated the marble-white convolutions around its head and middle flanks and underbelly. Orca himself, leader of a kill pack of a dozen of his kind, was in an ugly mood. That mysterious telepathy which every wild thing shares in degree had cleared the sea about him. It was as if disaster had forewarned of its coming, and all prey had fled. He noted the sea lions high on their rocks and grated his three dozen teeth in rage—

slasher fangs that had torn great whales apart and had
destroyed seals and porpoises in one crunch.

Orca was a true mammal—the same as all the whale and
porpoise tribes—warm-blooded and air-breathing. He ex-
pelled a cloud of spent vapor from his lungs with a geyser-
like whoosh, and pulled in draughts of fresh air. Then, with
an upheaval of water from the push of his powerful tail
flukes, he submerged.

The big killer whale could have caught fish had he
wanted, for the underwater shoals sheltered sizeable ling
cod and bass, while halibut and other bottom fish were
about. Some of his cohorts were feeding on these.

But Orca wanted larger prey. In Arctic waters his species
will smash into ice shelves to knock seals overboard. But
here the rocky reefs were impregnable, and the sea lions
were safe from attack—as long as they stayed out of water.
And well did they know it.

A red anger coursed through Orca's primordial brain.
He drove ahead into deeper water off Little River mouth.
And there he sighted a pair of blackfish—a harmless and
misnamed member of the porpoise family, sometimes mistaken for large sharks.

The terrified blackfish had no more chance than sheep
pursued by wolves. Orca bent to the pursuit with every
concentration of his powerful body—driven by that huge
horizontal oar which was his tail. He passed the smaller of
the two blackfish in disdain—let the others quarrel over
that one. In vain, the larger blackfish twisted and turned.
The relentless foe maneuvered equally well—and faster.

One chop of Orca's appalling teeth, and the blackfish was
half severed. In a murk of reddening water, the killer
gulped down his prey, leaving parts of it for others of his
band.

Satisfied in measure, he turned back toward the sea
lions' refuge. As he approached Trinidad Head, a flock of
brants settled upon the water some distance ahead. Orca

submerged and swung away from the rest of the pack. These tasty members of the goose family were to his liking.

The first inkling of peril the brants had was when the water about them seemed to bulge—but already it was too late for a couple of their flock. The survivors took to the air with frightened cries, while Orca chomped his jaws like a gourmet enjoying an especially delectable dish. He felt in better humor now.

Midfall was upon the land and sea—that time of year when gray whales start southward to bear their young and procreate in the warm waters of the Gulf of California, south of the United States border. From time beyond record, Orca's packs have known about this, and they will lurk in waiting off the coast line for these or any other whales that might appear. And so, the following day the sea lions again disported themselves in the area about Trinidad Head, for the killer pack had moved out to sea. Tension and foreboding no longer brooded over the water.

Orca and his grisly crew had timed it well. They were no more than ten miles from land when they became aware of a half dozen gray whales approaching from the north. The killers were in no hurry. They had ambushed whale schools before and knew their business. When the grays were within three hundred yards, Orca singled out the largest and drove full speed to the attack. The school scattered like stampeded cattle—except for its largest member. That animal was doomed. He thrashed and wallowed, apparently half-paralyzed from fear, while Orca—who was less than one third his bulk—tore again and again at his mouth and throat.

Had it been necessary, Orca could have handled this frightened monster by himself. But now he had more than enough help. In minutes, several killer whales were tearing and stripping hunks of flesh from their still living victim. A few hundred yards from this butchering, the rest of

Orca's band had surrounded another whale, and were churning the ocean's surface into bloody foam.

A shadow as large as a whale passed swiftly over the water, but even Orca paid it no heed, so engrossed were he and his pack. The source of that shadow was an airplane. In that machine, two men were peering downward at the sea in open-mouthed amazement. The pilot banked in a half circle and, this time, flew so low over the carnage that several of the killer whales dived in momentary alarm—but not Orca. Had the plane settled upon the water beside his kill, he would have attacked it without hesitation. Fear of the unknown was not yet included in his make-up.

But the sight of that slaughter had set certain nerve currents to work in the brains of the two men who had witnessed it. They circled the scene several times and then resumed course, talking excitedly. Gorged to satiety, the killer pack loafed in the vicinity of their massacre and after a time headed back toward the coast.

Calm weather had brought the trawler fleet out from nearby Eureka. Orca knew these bottom draggers. On occasion, he and his followers had raided their nets to fill up on sole and other fish conveniently bunched together there. The nets themselves were of no moment. If one of the pack got himself entangled, he ripped his way out like a bull bat from a spider web. All of which made the trawler men unhappy.

And so a climax occurred a couple of days later, when Orca's pack ran across the trawlers off Trinidad Head. Their whale feast had been digested and, for the moment, seals and their sea-lion relatives did not interest them. They bored down into the slow moving nets, packed with hapless fish, and ate their fill. Nor could the trawler men do anything about the matter.

One of the killer pack, a fifteen-foot female, committed the error of surfacing too near a boat. A volley of high-powered rifle bullets crashed into her head and back.

Frenzied and mortally hurt, she leaped out of water and dashed to and fro. Orca and some of the others were attracted by the commotion and rose to the surface some distance away. Bullets ricocheted about them, but none were hit.

Fortunately—for himself—Orca had no way of connecting cause and effect here, or he might have charged the boats and perhaps met his own end. He followed the dying female as she raced past him. Taste of her blood was in the water, but the killer pack was too well fed to turn cannibal. After a time, the female ceased her thrashing and lay inert. Orca and the rest of the pack left. None of the boats pursued them, since they were busy untangling their damaged nets.

Salmon were schooling off Humboldt Bay entrance, a few miles to the south—while seals and sea lions were among them. This made for good hunting. Later, they would put north to pay the Klamath River mouth a visit.

Orca liked these raids not alone for the variety of diet they offered—since sea birds and various fish also were available—but he especially enjoyed devouring large and toothsome salmon. Sport fishing boats were about the bay entrance, but these usually scuttled out of his way, and he paid them no heed.

An hour's slashing and killing off Humboldt Bar netted him a pair of fat seals and several salmon. The rest of the pack fared in ratio, while sportsmen retreated inside the bay channel.

By now, Orca's outstanding size was making him more or less noted. Both commercial and sports fishermen had passed the word to beware, while the two airmen had sighted him on several occasions.

Concerning all of this, Orca knew nothing—nor would it have interested him had he known. He was ruler not only of his raider gang, but owner of all the ocean he had swum in for some twenty years of life. He was the dominant male in his prime. To him, because of size and prowess, tribute was rendered. Sure of himself, he led the kills and ate the most. He had achieved success, and had grown into arrogance. . . .

It was off Castle Rock, near Trinidad Head, that Orca took issue with a boat. Two sportsmen were trolling for salmon in a small craft when one of then tied into a big king-chinook. The battle lasted for some time. Finally the fish began to tire. It rolled groggily on its side, some twenty feet from the fishermen's boat. And there, cruising just beneath the surface, Orca saw the silvery glint of its flanks. This was easy prey.

With a rush that made the water erupt, he rose and seized the exhausted salmon. He had no designs against the boat and would have ignored it but for one foolish act.

The fishermen had a light-gauge shotgun aboard, intended to pepper intruding sea lions or perhaps knock down a duck or brant. As Orca's black-and-white bulk showed partly out of water, the salmon loser's partner grabbed the weapon and sprayed bird shot into the monster.

This time, Orca connected cause and effect. He was not injured, but his ownership of the sea and all it contained was being challenged. He charged at the side of the boat, and all but turned it over. It was the fishermen's purest good fortune that their attacker still had a large salmon in his mouth, or he might have torn their craft apart. Bug-eyed with terror, they opened their high-speed outboard motor wide. The boat fairly skipped over the water, bounding and bouncing with every swell.

Orca finished his salmon in one gulp and took after the fleeing enemy that had dared defy him and cause pain. This thing, with its noise and churning, needed killing. He put on speed but was unable to overtake it. Thoroughly enraged now, he threw his entire strength into the chase and began gaining.

Had Orca found a chance to clamp onto that boat's fast revolving propeller, a tragedy would have occurred—although the killer would have lost some of his fearsome teeth in the fracas. But that, fortunately, was not to be. As Orca raised his head part way out of water and, mouth open, tried for the boat's stern, it skittered sidewise and again resumed its mad race for the shore. Fast though Orca was, the outboard had a slight advantage. Twice more this maneuver was repeated, with the boat escaping by inches both times. Then, as pursued and pursuer shot into the first line of surf where a sandy bottom showed beneath, Orca abandoned the chase. The boat leaped atop the breakers, saved from overturning by a miracle, and slid better than its length onto the beach. There it whipped sidewise and pitched its shaken occupants onto solid sand.

Orca was in an ugly mood. He was not accustomed to lese majesty from anything—let alone having the offender escape. He snapped at a young killer whale—perhaps one of his own progeny—that approached too near. He rushed to the surface to seize a sea gull that had just alighted, only to spit out the mangled bird in distaste. Orca wanted a change of diet—something to which he was not accustomed. He led the pack toward shore, where a kelp-bedded cove bespoke possible hunting. Seals on their southward migration might be found there, and fish were always abundant.

He was further stimulated, therefore, to encounter a group of furry animals huddled on the edge of the kelp bed, who seemed in fear of some enemy inside. They broke apart in panic as he approached—except for one that darted at him in an effort to turn him away.

Orca's anger arose. As lord and master of all the ocean, nothing should stand in his way. Deep in his dim and vengeful brain, the escape of that boat still rankled, while here was another prey that dared offer resistance. One chomp of his murderous jaws, and the life of a mother sea otter defending her baby was snuffed out like a candle flame in an explosion. Before the remainder of the sea-otter herd could lose themselves in the kelp beds' shelter, others fell prey to the killer pack.

But the sea-otter raid was only a tidbit for the marauders. Led by Orca, they headed upcoast for the Klamath River mouth, where they knew the salmon schools were homing into fresh water for their spawning runs.

The killers were in no especial hurry. The salmon's death saga meant only food to them. They overtook a herd of sea lions en route and enjoyed another blood-torn foray—which was elemental justice, since these predators were likewise seeking salmon.

Overhead, unbeknownst to the killer whales, a plane circled and banked. Its occupants were the same two men who had witnessed their gray-whale butchery. To the men the killers' outlines were clearly etched against the sea below. Their especial attention was concentrated upon Orca who, because of his size and place at the head of the pack, stood out like a lead wolf.

The whales were enjoying their ease in a calm sea. They loafed and rolled along the surface. Even Orca, who rarely indulged in cavorting, saw fit to relax.

Consequently, when an enormous bird swooped down upon them with a chattering roar, their surprise was complete. A spatter of bullets chopped the sea—unknown enemies that tore into a couple of the pack members with bloody effect. They leaped and raced about, much as the female who had been hit from the fishing boat. Like her, they expired and floated on the surface for a time before sinking into the depths. The remainder of the pack scattered when instinct warned them something was wrong.

Orca had submerged at once, and so missed a line of fire that was intended particularly for him. Perhaps his recent experience with the fishing boat had taught him a lesson. And perhaps he remembered that less recent affair with the trawlers, when a similar raking of the water had done away with one of his band. At all events he escaped unscathed and, for the first time, caution was making itself felt.

The hunt at Klamath River's mouth was all that the most ruthless of killers could have desired. Not only did the pack enjoy numbers of succulent salmon, but several sea lions and a small herd of seals fell victim to their forays. Their presence wrought havoc in the sea—much to the anger of sportsmen and game wardens alike.

By now, many men knew of the macabre leader of the killer whales. Among these was a coast-guard officer, stationed at the Klamath River mouth to prevent foolhardy sportsmen from losing their lives in the tidal currents. This man knew the sea. He was aware of the two fliers' efforts and had ideas of his own.

Consequently, communications flowed to higher echelons. In time, and after much slaughter of salmon, seals, sea lions, and—regrettably—sea otters, the experts behind the desk curtain passed upon the scheme—perhaps to get rid of its persistent proponent, for he had connections and knew how to use them.

Orca knew nothing of the turmoil and talk that he and his pack had been causing. The degree of caution he had acquired from recent experience was all but forgotten. The sea was calm and bountiful. One fall day, Orca was loafing off the Klamath River mouth, apart from the pack. He was feeling especially pleased with himself, for as he saw it, the Redwood Empire's classic autumn was his property. Perhaps he was planning conquests farther out to sea, where more whales were on their migration to the south. Perhaps he and his band might waylay a finback whale—that huge cetacean whose flesh would provide them a feast of grand proportions.

Overhead, one of those large and noisy birds was circling about. But since it did not alight upon the water to offer itself as prey, he was indifferent. When the bird buzzed rather closely overhead, Orca did not bother to submerge.

The surface was pleasant, this mild fall day, and he chose to bask.

Again it passed overhead—this time more closely and Orca swerved to one side in annoyance. As he did so, something landed in the water ahead with a splattering whack, skipped along the surface, and came to a stop. Mildly interested, Orca followed it. As he did, a taste of fresh-blooded meat permeated the water. He quickened his pace.

Orca approached the floating thing to investigate. It was small-seal size, and trailed blood in the water behind it. That blood tasted unlike anything he had known, and it drew him irresistibly. A measure of his one-time restraint warned, but he circled the bait with increasing interest.

A group of smelt arrived upon the scene—prey too insignificant for Orca's notice. The smelt began to nibble and jerk at the unknown morsel. That angered the killer king. He drove ahead and seized the missile with one positive clamp, scattering the smelt. And that was the last thing Orca knew. . . .

In the circling plane, the fliers and Coast Guard officer whacked one another's backs in elation as an explosion rent the sea below. A TNT bomb, wrapped in fresh-killed beef, had done the job.

Down into the depths off Father Klamath's mouth sank a shattered and headless thing that had been the terror of the deep, leaving a trail of blood behind it. Orca, monarch of the killers, was done, and the leaderless pack, torn with dissension and uncertainty, broke rank and went its several ways—vulnerable and no longer functioning as an entity.

Captive Set Free

Away to the west of the Valley of the Giants, on the sunset side of the Rainbow Mountains, there is a hidden valley. The Indians called it Mattole, which means clear water. Had they called it Bower of Plenty, favored of Manitou, their understatement would have varied only in degree.

Down the length of the Valley of the Mattole flows a river which wanders out to sea through a cut in the hills. Steelhead trout and king-chinook salmon school home to its waters at spawning time, while timbered mountains watch over the valley's domain. All manner of wild creatures live in its glens and vales. And spring-blossom time in the Mattole surpasses description.

Scant wonder the Indians loved this part of the Redwood Empire, and made it their especial Elysium—nor allowed white men to trespass until a bitter series of wars wrested it away from them. . . .

To a half-grown gray fox, however, the secluded sweep of the Mattole Valley meant nothing. For Pix was a prisoner, chained in a ranch yard since cubhood, when her family's den had been dug out and themselves destroyed. Chicken stealing had been the parent foxes' alleged crime—although in truth bobcats, coyotes, and horned owls were rather the sinners, with the fox family more sinned against.

And as though loss of freedom were not enough, Pix's existence depended upon the day-to-day whims of her master, a boy in his early teens whose mercy was not tempered with justice, or vice versa. Dogs had been encouraged to torment her, baited squirrel traps had been set to deceive her until she shrank from food, while often she was dragged from her kennel and goaded about for the pleasure of visiting youths.

As a psychiatrist might view it, Pix's budding individuality had been injured and warped beyond repair. In actuality, she had had a thorough series of lessons impressed upon her. At a tender age, she knew more about mankind than most wild creatures could ever learn.

All of this seemed unusable information, since Pix's life appeared forfeit to captivity and a premature end. But Manitou, who watches over wild things, had sent a messenger of mercy to whisper into ears which, at first, were deaf. But in time, repeated pleadings bore fruit. For the youth in question had an older sister who, with first stirrings of love within herself, felt pity for the captive who was being denied freedom and fulfillment.

And so it came to pass. The youth was attending a school function one evening. Sister's beau had come calling. And he, under the spell of feminine persuasion, saw the light.

When two large and hateful humans approached her kennel that night, Pix snarled and cried. With all her small strength, she resisted the all-too-familiar drag on the collar about her neck—but to no avail. When heavy hands seized her, she bit as valiantly was she could—but again to no avail. Those hands were covered with a skin that smelled like cattle and were beyond her power to reach.

One snip of a trap-smelling tool, and Pix's collar fell away. A deep voice shouted at her, while a higher-pitched one made cries she had heard used against garden-raiding chickens. For a moment, Pix was at loss to understand. Nothing like this ever had happened.

Then a dog barked questioningly. Both human beings yelled at him to be quiet. With that, comprehension in measure came. Like a wraith in the night Pix was gone— never to come near that place again.

While Pix's conscious self was confused by the turn of

events, her instincts were not. With the sureness of a guiding star, they led her away from the habitations, sounds, and smells of mankind. Ever thereafter, she avoided such places as a harried deer would shun the huntsman's camp. But she had much to learn about freedom and the price it exacted for survival.

Pix's first reaction was not unalloyed joy. Rather, she was beset by fear of the unknown and sought shelter in deep brush near the Mattole River. The valley's road ran near by, and she shrank when automobiles dashed past.

After a time, she became aware of the river. It was low from early fall's lack of rain—although the Mattole region is noted for heavy precipitation during the wetter half of the year. No road seemed to be on the other side of the river, nor were there any houses in sight. Also, a timbered draw appeared inviting, compared to the more open countryside around her. After some hesitation, plus a couple of false starts, Pix plunged through a riffle and swam to the opposite shore. Moments later she was into the fir woods.

This much gained, Pix began to take note of her surroundings. The draw ahead was rocky, which gave promise of hiding places. Outside of a cattle trail—probably started by deer ages ago—there was no evidence of mankind, although she still could hear an occasional vehicle across the river.

As night deepened, the road across the river quieted and the few ranch-house lights in the area went out. Somewhat reassured, Pix came out from shelter and began to cast about for provender. She was not long in locating a wood rat's nest in a willow clump. In moments, she had climbed the low tree and was tearing the nest apart—to partake of her first meal on her own.

Pix never had climbed a tree before—although she had scurried up fence posts around her kennel when harassed by dogs. But the instincts of her species played her true.

Generations of ancestors before her had climbed trees. She needed no instructions.

Quite refreshed now, and feeling more sure of herself, Pix set out to explore farther. Once she got a fright when a hare, half as large as herself, burst out of a grass clump. But that creature smelled of food rather than foe, and she made note to watch for its kind hereafter. Her wild-life education was almost a blank, since she had been captured while a small cub. But necessity for survival, together with native intelligence, were coming to her aid.

Break of dawn found Pix a half mile farther upstream. Here she climbed a formidable tower of rocks and sought shelter in a cave-den at its top. While her sense of smell told her that some creature had been there recently, it was not the odor of dogs, and she felt little concern. She was taking possession—and that was the essence of law.

Thus Pix fell into her first unpleasant encounter in the wild. Barely had she started to inspect the elevated hideout when a large and angry horned owl sailed into the entrance. Without hesitation Hush-wing charged, clopping his beak and striking with powerful talons.

Pix wanted none of this. She flattened herself against the side of the cave and scurried out—getting a talon rake as she did. Nor was Hush-wing satisfied even then. He swooped after her, swearing and hissing.

At some six or seven pounds weight, Pix was half again the heavier of the two. But the enemy was formidably armed, and his property rights were involved. She leaped down the rocks, dodging blows from the air as she went, and dashed into a wild blackberry thicket on the ground. Whereupon Hush-wing abandoned the chase and returned to his stronghold in vindication.

After a time, Pix emerged to seek a new shelter. Before long, she located a hollow log that smelled only of rabbits, where she denned up for the daylight hours. Thereafter she avoided places that carried odors of unknown occupancy, while her free life got its start.

Within a week, Pix had come to feel somewhat established in the wooded sector on the more isolated side of the Mattole River. She had found a den sheltered beneath an old log jam—and low enough that there would be no dispute with Hush-wing. In fact, it smelled faintly of her own kind, which assured her in degree.

Almost at once, Pix learned to dig out nests of mice and, after a couple of failures, ambushed a rabbit. Also, it must be said to her discredit—as mankind sees it—she had learned that certain birds roosted on the ground and could be caught by stealth. Several kinds of wild berries grew in abundance, as did tasty herbs and bulbs, and she reveled in the discovery of these new foods.

Already the bedraggled and hangdog appearance of her captivity was disappearing. Her fur, which varied from black and gray on top to reddish-brown on the sides and tawny beneath, was taking on a glossy sheen. Likewise, she was beginning to grow rapidly for the first time, and soon would attain adult size of some twelve pounds.

From the very start, Pix had been able to keep herself fed—which could be expected in a bounteous land like the Mattole Valley. Also, she was endowed with rather more acute sensibilities than most wild creatures.

Then, almost without prelude, the heavy rains that characterize the Mattole watershed started. To Pix, who had been born in April of that same year, and who had known only late-spring showers, this came as something of a shock.

First to be hit was her den under the old log jam. A torrent of water descended upon it, and she had to abandon it quite suddenly. Not for nothing had other animals shunned permanent residence there.

During the wetness that followed, Pix did the sensible thing. She climbed an oak tree and took up residence in a hollow therein. This involved a dispute with an opossum—

an animal transplanted to that area—which ended with the opposition's furnishing several meals. The little vixen fox was learning her way about.

With arrival of winter came Pix's first serious trouble. A pack of dogs of mixed ancestry were running half wild through the Mattole domain. They belonged to several cattle and sheep ranches thereabout but were law unto themselves. A couple of their number had been shot for killing sheep, but the others confined their efforts to running wild animals from bears and panthers to anything they could find—with deer and elk their especial prey.

Pix had heard them several times on the other side of the Mattole River and had tensed with fear and anger. But she considered these marauders removed from her sphere and would not have recrossed that stream under any circumstances. Now, with the river high and muddy, she felt secure.

What Pix had not discovered as yet was that the Mattole Valley's road crossed the river several times via bridges— an asset which the dogs, with wider range and long familiarity, used to their advantage.

One moonlit night, between storms, when Pix had climbed a tree to raid a wood rat's nest, a clamor broke loose near by. There was no question about it—that dog pack was on her side of the river. She froze amid the nest's rubble—a collection the size of a large hawk's nest—and lay low. Nor did she have to wait long. Within minutes, attracted by fresh fox scent on the ground, the pack arrived beneath the tree in full cry.

But the pack's supremacy ended at the tree's base. Yell, leap, and threaten though they might, their quarry was beyond reach. Nor could they see her, since Pix was curled atop the nest. After a number of noisy forays, punctuated by returns to the tree, the pack left. But the damage was done. They knew a fox was about and would return—a fact of which Pix was well aware.

Thereupon began an era of stress. Nothing could have tempted Pix to seek a den on the ground now. A hunted thing, she often huddled in the protection of her hollow oak by day and listened to the enemy below.

Most of the pack were not overly intent after one fox, since prey was plentiful everywhere. But one big mongrel hound felt differently. This one belonged to Pix's former ranch prison and had tormented her during her captivity. Before long, Pix knew she had an implacable foe. Nor would the area be large enough to contain them both.

During this period of siege, it was Pix's especial fortune that she could climb trees—an asset possessed by none of the canine tribe except a few species of fox. In fact, that asset was what saved her life, so relentless had become the mongrel hound's persecution.

Had that enemy from the ranch confined his efforts to daytime, he would not have been such a trial. But, as the pursuit intensified, the hound would stay near Pix's den-tree during parts of the night, even returning unexpectedly toward dawn. This made it necessary for Pix to give up her hollow oak at times and seek the nearest tree. Her foot scent was her betrayer, but she did not know what to do about it. Frequent rains helped, but every time she set foot on the ground between storms, the menace threatened again.

Finally, during a week of steady rainfall, Pix left the area of danger and headed up the Mattole River's flank. While on this shift of base, she again encountered a road traveled by automobiles. With security further upset—since she knew nothing of bridges—she fled to the timbered hills, away from the river's immediate proximity.

High in a wooded draw, she took up residence and awaited she knew not what. And this proved a stroke of fortune, for there she met Rex, a handsome male fox perhaps a year her senior.

At first, Pix was as terrified at sight of this larger animal as she would have been had she encountered another dog.

But when Rex climbed a tree after her, crooning gently instead of filling the woods with clamorous barking, she finally consented to touch noses. She had no conscious memories of her own kind, but instinct told her that here— for the first time—was a friend.

Thereafter she and Rex stayed within range of each other and hunted together at night. But for a daytime den, Pix was adamant. Only a tree would suffice, despite a puzzled Rex's dissent. Also, Rex seemed to favor staying closer to the Mattole River, with a tendency to work back downstream into the area Pix had left. She did not approve of this at first, but since the road had brought mankind too near again, she consented to forage as Rex seemed to want.

Pix's knowledge of throwing dogs off her trail was non-existent. However, under Rex's tutelage she learned quickly. Twice the dog pack—among whom was her mongrel-hound enemy—took after them. Pix climbed a tree at once, since this was the only safety she knew.

Rex, however, preferred to lead the dogs on a chase. He would circle and crisscross until he had the pack in a state of nerves. Then he would run up a small stream for perhaps a hundred yards, come out of it on one side and then the other—and retrace his downstream course to point of commencement. Had he been an army engineer plotting a strategy map, he could not have done better.

Thereupon, after several false starts to and from water, he would join Pix in a tree and watch the dogs try to puzzle it out. They might come to their very tree with much uproar —only to leave it again as others discovered more fox trails. To Rex, this was the essence of accomplishment.

It cannot be said that Pix enjoyed this game of hide-and-seek, but she was quick to realize its virtues—especially the trick of traveling up a small creek to kill scent. This last was a revelation. She might never have discovered it by herself, but the maneuver awakened age-old knowledge, and she benefited accordingly.

The gray fox's mating moon comes in late January. By this time, Pix had attained nearly full growth, and thanks to Rex's superior woodcraft, plus her own hard-earned knowledge of mankind and traps, she had become capable of handling almost any emergency—even to that ugly foe the mongrel hound, who still dogged their tracks.

The mating urge was another thing entirely. Until now, she and Rex had traveled together as companions. Now, suddenly, their status changed. She felt somewhat afraid of him at first but was drawn closer to him, and more significantly, than had been possible before. But she still insisted upon sleeping in a tree during the day—an act of which Rex disapproved but could not change.

Finally, however, Pix began to give way on this question, since instinct told her that a tree was not the right place in which to raise a litter of young—safe refuge though it was for herself.

With passing of the vernal equinox, the Mattole Valley's rains lessened. And with that time came Pix's home hunting, for she now understood that a den would be needed.

No prospective woman buyer could have been more particular in looking for a home than was this small female fox. Rex, her faithful spouse and partner, at times was exasperated—even as human husbands have been. But Pix knew what she wanted, and was determined to find it. That hateful hound-enemy must be thwarted. No compromise would do.

In time, she and Rex came to the foot of that tower of rocks where Hush-wing's stronghold was located, and from which Pix had been ejected on her first night of freedom. Although she was becoming heavy with young, Pix led Rex up the strenuous climb, rock by rock, until they reached the cave-den. She searched through it in apprehension at first, but its odors were stale and old. It was no longer occupied.

What neither fox could know was that Hush-wing had made one raid too many on the chickens belonging to the very ranch where Pix had been kept prisoner—and where the mongrel hound belonged. A steel trap, set by the same youth who had been Pix's jailer, had been the big owl's nemesis. The cave-den was now available.

And so, after a couple of days' further indecision and looking, Pix made up her mind and the foxes took possession. Thus two of Pix's former adversaries had proved a combined blessing—much to Rex's uncomprehending relief.

One of the last things Pix did before going into confinement in the cave-den atop the rock tower, was to add a chapter to Rex's store of information. Woodswise though her mate was, Rex had scant respect for, or fear of, mankind.

With the dominant male's assurance, Rex felt that such chattels as chickens were his legitimate prey—food to which he was entitled by right of landownership. Already, he had designs on the ranch across the Mattole River and down the road, where Pix and Hush-wing had been caught.

True, the river was too high as yet to swim in safety, but, in fox-language, Rex made his intentions plain. And his self-esteem was more than slightly dampened when his better half expressed disapproval that brooked no compromise. That ranch, with its human beings, dogs, guns, and traps was off limits for all times—forbidden without exception.

What the outcome of this difference of opinion might have been, no human being could guess—had it not been for a steel trap, cleverly set more than a mile upstream from the draw where the foxes' stone tower was located, and near the bridge. Pix and Rex were hunting together, rather beyond their usual range, when a tempting odor of chicken blood attracted them.

Mixed with that odor, however, was the dreaded smell of a steel trap—familiar to Pix but not especially respected by Rex. Pix was carrying a rabbit, freshly caught. Shaking with fear, but determined to show the peril involved, she approached the trap's leaf-buried center and dropped the rabbit into it.

Snap!—and the rabbit's carcass was seized. Both foxes sprang back in alarm. Then Pix did an even braver thing. She picked up the rabbit and trap and tried to disengage her recent prey. Fortunately, no other trap was set alongside, or her finish would have occurred then and there.

Rex watched, head cocked to one side, as she tried to take the rabbit away. Then he tried—but with no better result. The rabbit was held in a grip neither fox could break. Nor did Rex want it by then, for comprehension was dawning. This was bad; very bad. When Pix decided to leave, he followed willingly.

If a so-called dumb animal may be said to have been reflective, then that definition applied to Rex. Before he and Pix had gone many yards, he turned back to inspect that abandoned rabbit and the trap again. That was enough . . . Pix's demonstration had impressed him for all time. And Rex stood a better chance of living his allotted span because of it.

There remained now only the question of the dog pack and, more immediately, that mongrel hound whose especial hatred was Pix. A small stream of water flowed past the rock tower. This had helped Pix in choosing that location, for she had learned much from Rex. Trails were lost in that water, and the pair of foxes made use of it when approaching their chosen citadel.

Of course, an agile dog could climb the rock tower. But that was the chance all wild things must take. Likewise, the foxes had no recourse against mankind. Their one hope remained in not being discovered. And that meant getting rid of the mongrel hound.

. . . Then a miracle came to pass. Pix found herself mother to a pair of tiny, squirming, blind kit foxes. Another year, and she might bear three or four, but she was a young female, not entirely grown.

Springtime was coming to the Valley of the Mattole now, and April warmed the land. Food was abundant, and Rex, in his pride of family-support, fairly surpassed himself. But he was becoming a bit careless. He had not crossed the still-high river to raid the ranch's chickens—nor did he intend to do so, since he respected Pix's edict on that issue. And he remembered all too vividly the lesson of the steel trap. But Rex did not always take to the little stream for the last lap to the rock tower's base, especially if he was carrying a hare or other bulky prey. And so, one early dusk when he went down to hunt, he was met by a bellowing enemy bent on destroying the fox family.

The mongrel hound was no fool. For some time he had been working on this project, and now felt he was getting close to success, thanks to Rex's trail.

No tree climbing or trail mixing would be involved in this issue. It was either the hound or Rex. Away they went, with Rex leading the foe down the draw. In matters of strategy the fox was superior, but there was more at stake this time. That dog had come too close to the elevated cave-den. He knew too much now and must be destroyed.

For over a mile, Rex led his pursuer up the river bank toward the bridge over which the mongrel hound had come. It was no task to confuse him, but that would avail little now. As he ran and turned, Rex was deep into a problem he never had faced before.

Now a bear trap had been set in a declivity near the bridge—a heavy and murderous thing intended to catch a sheep killer. Rex had discovered it the previous night, and remembering what Pix had taught him, had given it wide berth. Now, decision made, he headed straight for it. A bit of judicious maneuvering gave Rex some respite when he arrived at the trap. He circled the menace with care, while studying its layout. By the time his foe arrived, the male fox was ready.

Apparently at bay and exhausted, Rex made a stand, dodging to and fro. Roaring with triumph, the mongrel hound rushed past the trap. Twice he did this, trying to get hold of that fox which seemed to escape his jaws by a fraction. The third time, sure of himself when his quarry staggered and all but fell, he charged through to the kill, and—clang!—a lethal thing seized him.

Rex did not stay to gloat. Leaving a doomed enemy to thrash and yell its life away, he put about and headed back for the rock tower. He was tired from the chase, and a nervous reaction set in that left him trembling. None the less, he ambushed a rabbit and bore it to his better half and progeny. The little ones were too young to touch solid food, but Pix was warmly appreciative. Although Rex lacked the ability to tell her in words, she knew at first glance what had happened. In fact, that mysterious telepathy which has been lost to humanity with its civilization had kept her in touch with him from the time the chase had started from the rock tower's base.

She crooned softly to her tired mate, happy in the knowledge they shared in common and through whose sharing they had won their battle. Rex lay down to rest and watched her at her meal. After a time, when he saw the rabbit was more than sufficient, he too partook. Henceforth he would be more careful in approaching their place of residence.

And so Pix, the once-abused captive, felt assured and happy with her family. She had a gallant mate to whom she was devoted. Spring was bringing beauty and new life to the Valley of the Mattole. Her worst enemy was gone. She cuddled her kits close to her and was content. . . .

Hush-Wing, the Indians called him, for his flight is like a shadow across the moon.

King of the Night

In the twilight of a redwood glen, Hush-wing, the great horned owl, watched dusk filter down with the setting sun. He was a deep-chested, powerful faunus, some two feet in height, with color blends that varied from barred-gray to whitish. His eyes looked frontward like those of a man— a trait unlike that of other birds—which, with his big tufted head, gave him an appearance of profundity he did not feel. For Hush-wing was baffled and disturbed.

To the owl, life was limited to three fundamentals; food, his mate, and the man-enemy. Food he understood, since that dealt with the primal want. But his mate was an entity apart from his decree, and because of that, he was at cross-purposes with her. A new nest location had to be found.

This problem had been forced upon Hush-wing by the one thing in nature he feared and was unable to understand— the man-enemy. Other creatures let him alone, or were in terror of him—but not man. Man meant death by traps and noise; dread dangers against which he knew no recourse. And now, man had taken away the big redwood tree where he and his mate had raised two or three fierce-eyed downy owlets each spring . . . had taken away part of the forest and left the pair of owls in a quandary.

Hush-wing had chosen another nesting site at once. There was a certain red-tailed hawks' aerie atop a tall redwood tree which he felt should belong to him. Although the hawks were quite as large as himself, the owl knew he could rout them day or night and take over their bower—a stronghold for the dusky gray king of the night and his consort.

But Hush-wing's mate had rejected the hawks' nest and chosen a large, hollow oak, high upon a ridge. It was felt that this tree, isolated from the redwoods in the glen below, would provide better safety . . . for in some intuitive manner the female owl sensed that the man-enemy planned to destroy the hawks' tree—even as that foe, given one chance, would destroy them.

Hush-wing brooded over this while the evensong twitterings of the day birds quieted down and ceased. Then he called to his mate. In the brush, over two hundred feet below, some small animal started with a muted shudder as inaudible to most ears as a feather fall. To the owl's acute hearing, the sound came clear as a twig snap. He peered down at it but decided to let it go.

He hooted again, and from a nearby tree came the answer, higher pitched possibly, and with five notes instead of his own four. For several minutes the two owls called back and forth, always with Hush-wing's four notes, and his mate's answering five. Then he spread velvet-lined wings and, with the lightness of elfin silk, floated down to a pool where he lit upon a rock.

His mate stayed back in the trees and called querulously for a time, but Hush-wing paid no attention. Let her come to him. . . . He waded into the water and drank once. Then he settled down, ruffling and swishing his feathers as a chicken would take a dust bath. An otter popped its head out of water to watch. Hush-wing stood up and snapped his beak with a hollow clop-clop. The otter submerged.

A shadow floated out of the blue dusk of the forest and dropped onto Hush-wing's vacated rock, soundless except for a touch of furred talons. For a moment his mate poised there to watch Hush-wing emerge from the pool and preen himself. Then they bobbed heads with a curtsylike gesture, and she stepped into the water.

Hush-wing took off with a downbeat that made swirls in the sand, but never a sound. He skimmed between the trees like a wraith, turning his lynxlike head to watch and listen. For now was the hunting hour.

In a few minutes he arrived at the hawks' nest with a wood rat still twitching in his talons. He did not expect to find the hawks in possession, since their nesting time came later than his own. He landed and began to tear his prey apart. In the midst of his meal, a wing tip cuffed him. His mate hovered overhead, cracking her beak. Her summons was not to be ignored. Hush-wing finished his breakfast with one gulp, crooning in appeasement. But his mate had left.

He wiped his beak on a sprig of growth and took to the air after her. The hour had arrived to settle the issue, he knew; for the January moon was new in the sky, and with its wane would come the horned owls' nesting period.

When they arrived at his mate's chosen oak tree, Hush-wing circled it in indecision. But his mate alighted at the entrance to the hollow and peered inside with feathers fiercely on end, lest a trespasser be there. Satisfied that all was well, she looked up at her willful spouse with a soft "crrooo?"

And with that, Hush-wing capitulated, since the female's choice in matters of residence was final. He alighted beside her and began a series of opera-bouffe bows. He sidled up to her, whickering in sly surmise, but she had turned coy and looked away. He catapulated into the air and turned a somersault with one muffled sweep of wing.

Hush-wing landed again, facing his mate, and raised every feather on end until he appeared twice natural size. He stalked up to her, chuckling like an aggressive rooster, and resumed his bowing. For answer, his mate turned her back and hopped to another limb, as if bored. Hush-wing followed, prancing on his toes and fluttering. She nipped him in annoyance, causing several feathers to float away, and dropped into the hollow tree. For a moment, Hush-wing looked like a too-ardent swain who had been slapped. Then he followed. . . .

Later in the evening, when a frost moon's beams slanted down the redwood aisles, Hush-wing began to hunt again. He was flying low between the trees, looking for creatures on the ground, when he felt a desire for trout. He swung over to the stream—to find a glare coming from his favorite pool. He ascended and lit in a tree close by. Down by the water's edge was a large fire. About it was a group of men and women, making the night unpleasant with their cries. During summer moons the owl had learned to expect this. But now, with winter's arrival, he felt he should again own that pool with its desirable fish.

A pair of these enemies left the fire and walked toward Hush-wing's tree, making courtship sounds of their own. The owl felt worried and angry. Through his consciousness surged a hatred for these trespassers who, as he saw them, could only mean harm. He glared down and gave out a groan of wrath, followed by a shriek that rent the air like a death cry from outer darkness.

Results were instantaneous. The smaller of the pair screamed and dashed back to the fire. The other ran after her. The whole group began to gabble like excited chickens. Then a loud bang shattered the forest's echoes. Hush-wing knew what that meant. He took to his wings.

But when the group had gone, Hush-wing felt vindicated. Once again he owned his glen valley with its stream. As a result, his primacy was particularly outraged when he went back to the oak and found a large male owl whickering at his mate, who was staring at him from the hollow.

Hush-wing dove for the intruder, cracking his beak like a backfiring plane. But the enemy was fashioned of lusty sinew himself, and knew what he wanted. He rocketed upward, to collide with Hush-wing in mid-air. The two powerful birds fell to the ground with talons interlocked, each pounding his wings and trying to destroy the other's eyes with his own steel-shears beak. The female owl stayed in the entrance of the nest-to-be, tensed and watching. Had the enemy shown signs of winning, she would have gone to Hush-wing's rescue, for they, like most owls, were mated for life.

Hush-wing was fighting with every atom of his threatened being. When, in time, an opening came, he struck deep into one of his foe's crystalline-glowing eyes. That eye burst like a broken light globe. In its place gaped a ragged socket. Hush-wing drove for the remaining eye with maddened strength, lusting to destroy it and smash through into the brain behind.

But the intruder had had enough. He began to twist and squirm, averting his head and racing his wings until he got himself into the air . . . whereupon Hush-wing let go and launched an aerial attack. Banking and diving, he drove his recent rival across the glen-valley and away. After a tour of inspection, he put back to the oak, where he gave his mate a vigorous nip for general discipline's sake.

. . . Now that their new abode was established, the female owl no longer seemed interested in the redwoods down in the glen. Possibly from instinct, but more probably to keep her mate reminded, she began to sleep in the hollow oak by day—although it would be a fortnight before the first large white egg was laid. On rainy days, Hush-wing stayed in the hollow with her; but more often he slept outside, where he was awakened frequently by his sensitive hearing. He did not yet trust this place, for always he had lived deep in the redwoods, and by comparison the oak seemed exposed.

At the lower end of Hush-wing's glen valley, the hills came close together. The stream foamed through a narrow gorge into a valley beyond. In this larger area lived a colony of man-enemies. Hush-wing knew their farms of old—and knew where they kept their chickens. For the most part, however, these birds seemed to hide in inaccessible dwell-

ings. But now and then an unwary chicken might roost in a
tree, or one of their dwellings would be open.

This was on Hush-wing's mind one black and storm-
blown night. His mate already had laid her eggs, three in
number. He had taken her place on the nest to let her go
out and hunt. But a downpour was falling, and she soon
returned, hungry and wet. This was not good, Hush-wing
felt, although poor hunting came with the rain time. He
decided to go down to the man-enemy's valley and bring
back a chicken for his mate and himself to enjoy in the
dryness of their hollow tree. He was beginning to forget
the hawks' nest now and accepted the benefits of shelter as
his due.

He left the nest and drove into the storm. In minutes, he
was over the man-enemy's valley, heading for the farm where
he had had good hunting in the past. This place seemed
different from the rest. Only one man-enemy appeared to
belong there, instead of a noisy crowd. This man-enemy was
quiet, and his surroundings more like the woods. Also, if
there were chickens about, some might be found in trees or
at large, instead of hiding in coops.

He arrived and stopped in a tree near the yard to reconnoiter. But no chickens were roosting there, and the
place seemed deserted and storm-lashed. A lone light shone
from the little drab-colored dwelling of the man-enemy.

The door to an unpainted barn was open. From it came
a chorus of subdued sounds, audible even above the wind.
Hush-wing never had ventured into that barn because it
looked like a man-enemy's dwelling. But the noises interested him, and he shifted to a tall fence post on the barn's
lee side, the better to appraise the situation. While there,
he heard the sleepy cluck-cluck of a chicken.

For a time, he sat statuelike on his new watch-post. Then
he floated silently through the open door to look. A cat,
that had been groping in the hay for mice, left in a scared
hurry.

Hush-wing circled in and out of the barn several times before deciding to land on a rafter. At first he listened with the guilty alertness of a burglar. A flock of chickens were at roost on a crossbeam. Although they could neither see nor hear the owl, they were becoming restless. One of them let out an alarmed cackle. Hush-wing could hear its heartbeat quicken when he selected it for the kill. He seized the cackler, severed its head with one bite, and shot out into the storm with the flopping carcass.

A hubbub of squawking broke loose in the barn. A dog began to bark. In the man-enemy's dwelling, the light brightened.

For several days after that, Hush-wing let the chickens alone. Then, on a breathless overcast night when nothing seemed about, he decided to bring in another. All appeared quiet at the farm. The barn still gaped open, unlike most chicken hiding places. But age-old owl ritual decreed that he listen and observe before acting.

He lit on his watch post with the silence of dewfall and —Snap!—something seized his ankle as no foe ever had gripped him. He leaped with a beat of powerful wings, but the post hung on. He bit in fury at the thing that had hold of him, but it was as cold and unyielding as rock. Again and again he struck at it, until his beak was chipped and his tongue bleeding. The dog began to bark.

Hush-wing's rage was turning into panic. For once there seemed nothing he could do. Flight was denied him. And a light had come from the man-enemy's dwelling and was moving toward him.

Two men arrived at the post. They shone a searing beam up into Hush-wing's face. He felt his eyes ache with shock as the sensitive irises contracted. He swelled his feathers to fantastic proportions and lunged down at them, snapping his beak in a bloody froth from his injured tongue.

One of the men laughed. "Well, your squirrel trap deal paid off, all right. Say, he's a tough hombre, eh?"

"They all are," said the other. "Ain't a wickeder varmint. You sure you want him? I'd ruther kill him right off."

"You bet I want him!" replied the visitor. "I'll take him home to the city. Bring-'em-back-alive; that's me."

Hush-wing sensed the man-enemies were undecided in some manner, but to his mind that meant only how they were going to kill him. So when one of them reached up and took hold of a wing tip, he tried as never before to get at his captors. He cracked his beak with tommy-gun speed and lunged back and forth. But the trap was well fastened to the top of the post, and it held him helpless.

"Now," said the man who had hold of the big owl's wing, "you grab hold of his other tip like I've done, an' I'll press down on the trap spring with this hoe. An' for God's sake hold fast when he pulls loose, or he'll come down on top of me. Watch yourself!"

In a matter of moments, Hush-wing found himself being carried by the tips of his wings, with his body dangling puppetlike between. And twist and threaten though he might, the man-enemies held him as they wanted. They opened the end of a chicken house and tossed him into it.

Hush-wing did not even touch the floor. With one surge of his wings he flung himself toward the open . . . and struck something that resembled an age-coated spider web, but which was strong beyond all understanding. He clung to it, beating his wings, while his captors watched outside. After a time he let go and dropped to the floor, blinking into the light with pupils shrunk to dot size. But when the men-enemies came closer, he hurled himself against the barrier and challenged them to fight to the end, as noblesse primeval should.

"Think we can tame him?" asked the man who wanted him alive.

"Never in a million years," stated the other. "You gotta get 'em plenty young for that, an' then it's damn' near impossible."

"Say," said the first, "I'll bet he's got a nest in these hills somewhere, eh?"

"He sure has," replied his host. "Why don't you try an' find it an' get you a young'un to take home? Then we can kill this one."

"Good idea," said the city man. "Know any places to look?"

"Yeh, I think so. An' I'll help you."

Ten days passed, and Hush-wing was slowly dying. Although the men brought food in abundance, he scorned most of it. Even the water they set out seemed hateful, and he drank little. During the nights, he tried without cessation to find a way to break through that web which was so strong. Time and again he searched every part of his prison in futility. Daylight would find him exhausted and withdrawn into the darkest corner—but ready to fight if the man-enemies came near. And in front of him, in full view, was freedom—the woods and hills—with only that heartbreaking barrier between.

On the tenth night, a subdued five-noted call sounded near by. Hush-wing answered instantly, and his mate alighted on the ground in front of the cage. But theirs was no joyous reunion. At that day's end, the man-enemies had discovered the hollow oak. They had tried to climb the tree, but she attacked them so savagely in the oncoming dusk that they had left, after shouting and throwing missiles.

Daylight would bring them back with the danger-that-kills-by-noise; she knew. Hush-wing trembled with weakness and rage as he became aware of his mate's extremity. He flung himself at one corner of the wire which had seemed to weaken of recent nights. His mate watched at first. Then she took hold of it from the outside with her talons. From her vantage point, the leverage was better—and she was quite the stronger now. A rust-eaten staple pulled out. One corner of the wire peeled back. Hush-wing tried at once to push his head through the opening they had made, but it was too small. He struggled in frenzy for a time—to quit at the end, exhausted.

By now, his mate seemed to have decided this strange web had a vulnerable point. She was attacking the corner with much buffeting of wings and biting at the curled wire . . . when the man-enemies' dog heard her and arrived, barking. Hush-wing's mate took to the air, dove onto him, and raked his back with her talons and beak. The dog fled for the house, yelping murder. Out hurried the man-enemies with lights. The female owl circled overhead and flew away.

The men were puzzled. "I can't figure what kinda varmint done it," the dog's owner said, examining his pet's wounds. "We better take him inside an' dress them cuts. Say, how's the owl?"

"Oh, he's all right. Looks half dead," said the city man, who had glanced into Hush-wing's cage. "I'll be glad when we can kill him tomorrow. If we'd just had a gun at that nest tree tonight—"

"We'll fill her with buckshot first thing in the morning," his host promised grimly. "They're blind as a bat in the daytime."

For a while, the two men poked about the premises. Then they went back into the house, taking the dog with them.

Not long after the door closed, Hush-wing's mate returned. But now they seemed to have lost their co-ordination, and see-sawed back and forth, with Hush-wing tottering at times.

After a lapse of futility, his attention focused once more upon the peeled-back corner of the wire. Again he tried to push through. His mate watched until he gave up, panting with weakness. Then, as if inspired, she seized the wire's end with one talon, braced, and pulled with all her strength. A piece of rotting wood gave way . . . and with it a foot of wire peeled back.

For a moment, both birds were startled by the enlarged opening that had come. Then Hush-wing came to life with a burst of reserve strength. He dove into the gap, losing a handful of feathers in his hurry, and tumbled onto the ground outside . . . free!

With never a glance behind, the pair of owls winged away into the night.

The first thing Hush-wing wanted was food. A half mile back in the hills, he spied a large weasel. He swooped, killing it with a single blow. A renewed vitality pulsed into his starved body with each beakful of warm, pungent flesh. He took to the air again on freshened wings and headed for the nest. On the way, he picked up a wood rat for the young he had not yet seen.

He arrived at the nest to find his mate already there. She had brought back a half-grown duck in an unwitting gesture against man-enemies and their possessions. Two balls of white down with great eyes and absurdly oversize feet were bickering over their meal. But the third egg lay cold where it had been pushed into a corner of the nest. Nor was it ever destined to hatch, for owls lay their eggs a few days apart but start setting as soon as the first one appears. And this final egg had been neglected too often while the female owl hunted the owlets' food and looked for her mate.

For a time, the pair of owls watched their broodlings and felt content to be together again. Then a soundless accord passed between them. Hush-wing took off across the glen valley to the redwood tree with the hawks' nest. He found the aerie not yet occupied, although it had been lined with feathers and repaired. After a detailed inspection, and ridding it of the feathers, he returned to the oak.

Tenderly his mate picked up one of the fledglings in her talons. Hush-wing took the other with a grip that had turned to furred cushions, and away they flew. In a matter of minutes, nest-keeping had been set up in the once rejected location.

In the dark before dawn, Hush-wing sat beside the former hawks' nest. He felt pleased with the paean of his deep-toned voice across the glen valley. Again he was king of the night, in command of his domain—and this time in the abode of his choice.

That he had been the cause of all the trouble . . . and that this might be only an interlude . . . was beyond his capacity to understand. All he knew was that he had had much to eat during the night, and enjoyed the feel of vibrant energy that was recharging his strong-knit body. In a few minutes now, he would hunt up those hawks and drive them from his redwood vale forever.

And in the deserted hollow oak there remained only a cold and dead egg for the man-enemies in the morning.